Christophe
BVSc MRC\

 C000081669

Chris graduated from Bristol Vet School in July 2007. Amongst his innumerable achievements during his time at Bristol, Chris was elected as president of Centaur, the Veterinary Student Society. For reasons best known to him only, he also studied for and graduated with an intercalated BSc (Hons) in Biochemistry. At present, Chris works as a small animal vet in Oxford and enjoys all aspects of medicine and surgery. Whilst the lifestyle of a Veterinary Surgeon is not entirely conducive to a hectic social calendar, Chris maintains that he still regularly enjoys both climbing and fencing. You are most likely to spot him sitting in an old Oxford café, contemplating life and penning his next bestselling book.

Matthew Swaffield

Matt started at Bristol Vet School in 2005 and is currently undertaking an intercalated BSc degree in Veterinary Pathogenesis. He is due to graduate as a vet in 2011, assuming everything goes to plan. Matt intends to enter small animal practice after university and is very much looking forward to finally receiving his first pay-cheque although will settle for a box of chocolates from a satisfied client! He is currently President of Centaur, the Bristol Vet School society, and enjoys playing rugby (from a safe distance), partying away his student loan and, randomly, Nigella Lawson.

The authors would like to thank the following: Caroline and Kate Parkinson for their incredible illustrations; Becky Fisher for her advice, proof-reading and general awesomeness; Dr Lynda Moore for her preface; and all of the amazing people who agreed to be interviewed for this book. Without you all this book would never have been!

Contents

Preface to First Edition

My initial thoughts when Chris and Matt asked me to write this preface were somewhat mischievous – after all, as an Admissions Tutor, did I really want all our "secrets" made public?! However, having read the book I find myself unable to play devil's advocate because I am so full of admiration for the job they have done. These two young men have taken what can be a dry and factual subject (I know, I give talks on it at Open Days!) and produced a stimulating text full of tips and hints which only those who have been through the process can really know.

"Vet School" is written in a style which is easy to read and digest. It is personal whilst being informative, with some very down-to-earth language in places! It is totally realistic and full of home truths, both from the authors' own experiences and those of other students and graduates whose profiles are used to illustrate the text.

The entire subject of achieving a place at Vet School, what to expect once there and the profession in general is tackled in a no-holds-barred, logical fashion, with good clear explanations of the intricacies. The initial sections invite you to examine your suitability to be a vet and require some important soul-searching. Following this are chapters on work-experience and academic requirements, how to complete the UCAS form including the all-important personal statement, and even tips of the choice of different vet schools in the UK. The information on interviews provides food for thought in terms of possible questions and areas to research. At all times, the authors avoid simply listing the facts and the subsequent discussion often reads like an informal chat in the student common room (not that members of staff eavesdrop, you understand!). The whole book is definitely designed to get you thinking "out of the box" and beyond the ordinary, just to push yourself a little further – which is no bad thing for a future vet.

Whilst this is a book written for students by students (past and present), it will be equally interesting for the grown-ups! We all recognise the supportive role played by parents and guardians throughout the years, both before and during University. The tips on organising work experience and the section on financing veterinary studies will be essential reading, the latter particularly in the current climate of top-up fees and student loans. I also seriously believe that every sixth form teacher should read this book and that no careers library should be without a copy.

Having known Chris and Matt for several years now, I am not at all surprised that they decided to write this book. Both have been heavily involved in student support at the University of Bristol and also with local and national recruiting events. This venture therefore comes not from a desire to "get rich quick" but as a serious attempt to use their own experiences to help potential veterinary students for years to come. It is my opinion that actually the book will do two things: it will make the life of an Admissions Tutor even harder (I forgive you lads!) but more importantly, it will provide students with all the ammunition they need to help them turn their dream of achieving a place at Vet School and all that follows on from it, into a reality. So – the authors have done their bit and now it is down to you - good luck!

Dr Lynda Moore
Veterinary Admissions Tutor & Senior Lecturer
Bristol Veterinary School

Why Veterinary?

"So, why do you want to be a vet?" This is the classic question which you will be asked more than a hundred times, not only during the application process but all the way through your careers as well. Why then do you really want to be a vet? Is it so you can live the stereotypical James Herriot lifestyle treating wayward lambs and driving through the great outdoors en route to call-outs? Maybe you have a burning desire to be the world's top small animal orthopaedic surgeon and spend your time working in referral practice or at a university developing new and novel surgical techniques, teaching students and peers, and giving presentations at numerous conferences all over the world. Of course, you could simply wish to have a quiet life working as the local horse vet, administering vaccines and advising people on equine healthcare. We could spend the entire book listing such possible career scenarios but hopefully it will suffice to say that a career in veterinary medicine offers an incredibly varied one in which the possibilities really are virtually endless. A veterinary degree doesn't, however, mean that you have to spend your entire career working in practice, or even working with animals full-stop. It is commonly acknowledged that the degree offers one of the best all round scientific educations available and equips graduates with the skills and expertise to do, well, almost any job you can really think of.

What motivates someone to want to be a vet? I am hazarding a guess that one of the primary motivators for you is that you like animals. Yes? Good. Well, it's obviously an important part of the whole case for being a vet but certainly is not the only one. There is, for a start, a real difference between 'liking' animals and being able to work with them on a daily basis, especially when a healthy proportion of those animal patients you treat want to bite, scratch and generally not be around you. Being a vet, and certainly training as one, is definitely not a licence to just spend all day stroking cute puppies and cradling cuddly kittens. It can be a tiring job, with long hours, a lot of stress, especially when dealing with ever increasing client expectations, and is often a dirty, messy job – try working as a cattle vet and not getting covered in s%*t! If money is what motivates you then you're probably better off thinking of applying to medical school or doing a degree in economics and entering investment banking. It is a commonly held misconception that vets are all multimillionaires and drive into work each day in their Aston Martins before heading back to their spacious riverside penthouse apartments to spend the evening supping on fine vintage champagne. The truth, however, is very different. One of the main reasons for this publicly held belief is that clients don't really make the distinction between their animal's healthcare, which is private and therefore has to be paid for, and their own experience of healthcare, which is, more often than not, provided free of charge by the NHS. What people don't remember – and certainly never at the time of being asked to pay for that 'hideously expensive' pyometra operation – is that they DO pay for their own healthcare, and do so handsomely through the wonder of taxes. Imagine a National *Animal* Health Service.... it would be blissful! So what do vets actually get paid then? That's a very broad question as there are so many potential career paths that a vet can take. However, considering that 80% of new veterinary graduates enter clinical practice after graduating it seems sensible to consider the earnings of this group initially. The average starting salary in 2007 for vets in general practice in the UK was around the £21,000 mark. This figure can vary depending on which part of the country you're in, whether you're expected to be on-call, whether the job comes with a house and/ or car and which perks may be offered as part of the overall 'package.' One of the authors, for example, started with a salary of £28,000 before tax, with accommodation provided for the first three months, a CPD (continued professional development) allowance of £1000 and 5 days a year, the payment of Royal College of Veterinary Surgeons (RCVS) registration fees (this has to be paid each year to retain the title MRCVS and therefore the right to practice as a vet), annual subscription to one association/ publication (for example, the BSAVA), and 20 days of annual paid leave. Some of the authors' friends started on more or less money but may have been 'given' a car or a house as part of the package thus meaning that they wouldn't need to pay those expenses out of their own pockets. One thing to remember is that as a student it is very easy to get used to not having to pay tax and as such that first pay-cheque can be a bittersweet experience as you jump for joy at the first figure you see (the gross amount you've earned that month) only to be depressed by the following figures showing how much the government has decided it wants to have from you for National Insurance and income tax. Oh, and then there's the good old student loan contributions, which start being automatically deducted from your salary the April following graduation. As such, it's not unreasonable to expect your net (after tax) salary to be about 30% less than your gross (before tax) amount. That £28,000 is, in reality, and when I say 'reality' I mean that you get to actually put it in your pocket and spend it, more like £19,000 a year. Quite different and important to consider when, firstly, deciding whether this is a career for you and, secondly, when deciding on jobs as a newly qualified vet. As far as starting salaries go vets actually don't fare too badly though, with FY1 doctors paid an average of £19,000 a year and the average graduate starting salary something similar. However, it is generally true that five years into your career you can expect to be earning less than your medical, legal and dental peers. A salary of £35-40k as a 5-10 year qualified vet seems to be the average at the time of writing but when you compare that to the £60-100k that equivalently experienced doctors will be earning then it becomes clear that if it's money that primarily motivates you then perhaps a medical or legal career is more your thing. What about earnings as a specialist? Surely they earn more? Well, yes, they do but then again so they should. After all, to become a recognised veterinary specialist, which more often than not requires a vet to have a diploma, vets have to commit to extensive post-graduate training, often at their own expense, and which very often involves a relative cut in their salary for the duration of their training. A small animal medicine specialist we know studied for three years, and worked his socks off, at one of the veterinary schools to achieve his diploma and was being paid a paltry £14k a year, albeit tax-free. Granted, when he did eventually pass and was able to get a job in private referral practice he was able to expect about £60k a year but compare that, again, to the equivalent in medicine where specialists will be expecting to earn far in excess of this figure. It seems that to really make decent money in private practice one has to become a partner but then this involves making a huge investment in a practice, and likely having to take on business administration responsibilities at the expense of purely clinical work, so it's not realistically a route that is open to the majority of graduates until a good few years into their careers. What about other career paths in veterinary? What do they earn? Well, vets in industry such as those working for pharmaceutical companies may be expected to earn more than those in practice, and can likely expect a more 'normal' lifestyle with regards hours worked (ie. '9 to 5').

If we haven't managed to put you off veterinary as a career by now then there's a good chance that no one is going to be able to. In this case, grab a cup of coffee and a comfy seat and enjoy this book, which has been written for you by two people who have been in the exact same position that you find yourself now. As such please be reassured that it isn't impossible to get into vet school – in fact, when you see some of the people they do actually let in you'll really appreciate this – and that by picking up this little publication you're making proactive steps towards realising your goals. Good luck and enjoy the read.

There are a variety of sources of further information available if you are keen to really explore veterinary as a possible career option, including a number of 'courses' and experience-days run by various companies and the vet schools themselves. Examples of these include:

1. **VetMedlink & Vetsim** – run by The Workshop in Nottingham each Christmas and Summer
    (*www.workshop-uk.com/vetmedlink.php*)
2. **Vetquest** – held each Spring at Bristol University
    (*www.vetschool.bris.ac.uk/langford/contedu/vetquest*)
3. **VetCam** - run each Spring in Cambridge
    (*www.vet.cam.ac.uk/application/opendays.html*)

Although these courses can offer some insight into veterinary as a career option and are actually good fun, they are no substitute for work experience and we advise students to focus their main efforts on completing a good range of work placements, and to study hard.

What are my chances of getting in to Vet School?

The answer to this is 'better than you were probably expecting.' Chances are you've heard horror stories of how there are about a million applicants to every place and that you need to have a PhD before you're even considered for interview. This is, in no uncertain terms, crap! Yes, it's a very competitive course which partly stems from the fact that it's a difficult and challenging training programme and so requires applicants to demonstrate a very high standard of academic ability but also from the simple fact that there aren't really that many places available for wannabe vets. At the time of publication there were 8 vet schools in the UK and Ireland: The Royal Veterinary College in London, Bristol, Cambridge,

Nottingham (the newest of the bunch), Liverpool, Edinburgh, Glasgow and Dublin. With the exception of London, which trains approximately 270 new vets per year, the other schools have intakes of about 100 students each year. Using our incredibly honed maths skills tells us that there are, therefore, roughly 900 places up for grabs each year for prospective vets. Compare this to medicine where you have about 32 medical schools, each training about 300 students a year and it'll soon become apparent why vet school is so much harder to get into. So yes, you have to be special to get that hallowed place but not as special as the urban rumours would have you believe. In terms of the type of student applying to vet school the vast majority are female, with the current ratio of graduates standing at 70:30 female to male, quite a contrast to previous years when veterinary was very much a male dominated profession. For more detailed information on the number and type of student at each vet school see the appendix at the end of the book.

Each vet school will have an allotted number of places reserved for different 'types' of student such as graduates, international students and then standard home students. One of the reasons the vet schools, and indeed any university course, will keep a number of places specifically for international students and graduates is that, first of all, they pay considerably more than standard home students will, with annual fees for veterinary typically being in the £20k a year region compared to the £3-4k that home students will pay in tuition fees. As such, they represent a fairly lucrative sector of the market for universities and with the cost of research and running universities ever increasing this extra money comes in very handy. The other benefit for the universities is that it broadens the appeal, both internationally and at home, of the school and so is excellent marketing. However, the vast majority of places available at UK vet schools will go to standard home students so fear not.

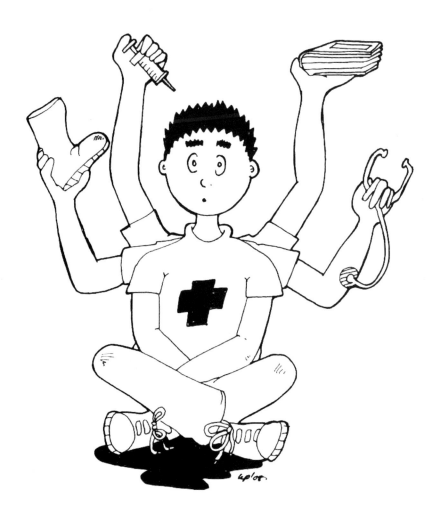

What attributes do I need to be a vet?

The key attribute you need in bucket-loads in order to get into vet school in the first place and then actually finish the course is determination. Many of you will, I am sure, be told by careers advisors that you simply aren't the right type of person for veterinary as you may not have the grades (at the moment) or perhaps don't have the work-experience (yet). Chances are that the advisor simply hasn't got a clue about veterinary as a career and course and so rather than admitting this would rather just attempt to steer you away from a career path that you instinctively know to be right for you. At the end of the day you are the only person who is going to get yourself into vet school and you will need all the grit and determination you can muster to achieve this. For starters you need top grades across the board, but especially in the sciences, maths and English at GCSE, and then at least chemistry at A-level or an equivalent. Then you need to demonstrate your commitment to veterinary as a career by showing evidence of a broad ranging work experience, with good placements proving harder to secure each year. After ticking these boxes – and let's face facts here that most of the other thousand or so applicants will have managed to tick these – you then need to show the selectors that you are in fact an interesting and 'well rounded' individual and not a dull bookworm who only leaves the confines of your desk to either visit the loo or sleep. This is achieved by demonstrating evidence of extracurricular interests and pursuits. The reason for this is very simple when you think about it. The veterinary course is tough and intense. Fact. You need to work hard. True. But if all you do is work, work, work then there is a good chance you will crack under the pressures of both the studying involved and the huge lifestyle change that accompanies going to university. The adage that vets 'work hard but play harder' is true and is an important part of staying sane at vet school. Those students who do just devote themselves 110% to the rigours of academia for 5-6 years and never let their hair down or engage in some moderately non-vetty activity tend to finish university either as sad, lonely shells who will have very real difficulty adjusting to life in clinical practice or will, potentially, not finish the course at all due to burning out. So, if you play hockey at weekends or have a band but are contemplating giving up your favourite hobbies so you can focus completely on your studies then my advice is "don't!" The key word is 'balance.' If you're worried that your grades are slipping and you currently play pool every single night of the week then, yes, trim back to a couple of nights and focus more on the books. Chances are that you will need to trim back and better organise your time if you are to fit in the work experience that is expected of you. So, another set of attributes that you'll need are both organisation and motivation.

What type of person makes a good vet?

There is no steadfast mold that every vet fits neatly into, which is a good thing especially as the profession is such a varied one. However, there are certain character traits that do seem to be important:

1. Sense of humour – it is vital that you have one of these, especially when you consider that on at least one occasion you will be expected to respond to an emergency call-out at some insanely early hour in the morning, often to find that the supposed 'emergency' was in fact a simple case of belly-ache! If you're not able to laugh off situations like this then it's highly likely that veterinary will rapidly wear you down and depress you.

2. Good communication – it is becoming recognised more and more both in human and veterinary medicine that the difference between a good doctor and a great doctor is effective communication skills. You could be the font of all knowledge, having hoovered up every relevant text on all subjects, but if you are unable to relay that information to clients in an appropriate manner then it will count for nothing. Often the best medics are those who don't know everything – and importantly, recognise this fact – but who are empathetic, can listen well and then explain things to clients calmly and in terms that non-medically trained people will understand. The VDS (Veterinary Defence Society – the guys who stand up for vets when we get sued) reported that the vast majority of complaints against vets arise as a result of a failure of communication. This can be as simple as discussing a potential surgical procedure with an owner and not recognising or checking whether the owner actually does understand, despite their enthusiastic head-nodding. A good communicator in this case would present the options calmly, regularly checking for understanding and then asking the owner whether they have any questions. One of the toughest consults to face, and the one where good communication can be key, is euthanasia. The experience of the authors is that the majority of owners will understandably be very upset, will possibly be feeling guilty about their decision and as a result may not be in the best frame of mind to listen. They will also be much more sensitive to things that are happening both to themselves and to their beloved pet. As such it is vital that you approach the consult with empathy, both in terms of adopting a sympathetic, non-judgemental voice tone and open body language (ie not sitting behind a table with arms folded), and explain to owners exactly what is going to happen. We find that if an owner has been advised of what may happen, even if it is unpleasant, then if it does occur they are less likely to freak out and ultimately blame you. The classic approach we take in these consults is to, first of all, commend the owner on their courage in making such a tough decision and reassuring the owner that it is in the best interests of their pet, then very calmly explain what needs to happen. For example, "what we will do, with the help of one of my nurses, is to clip a small area of fur from Pooky's leg, and place a small catheter so that he/she can then relax with you. What we will then do is to give Pooky an injection of anaesthetic so that he/she gently drifts off to sleep peacefully but will not wake up." This reassures owners of the reasons for why you want to remove their soon to be departed pet from them for a few minutes, and then further reassures them that the process itself is peaceful and painless - the primary concern for owners. Advising owners of what can potentially not go to plan is a good idea despite instincts suggesting that this is the last thing owners want to hear. However, it is far better that an owner be warned that their pet may, unconsciously (and ensure that you make this fact clear to owners) urinate or poo, or may take a gasp, than for it happen midway through a euthanasia at which point an unprepared and emotional owner is likely to panic, thinking that their pet is still alive and suffering. Preparing an owner for all eventualities is one of the key communicative tools at our disposal and can result in the owner leaving the room either thinking that you are a kind and empathetic vet or a butchering monster. The ability to be able to communicate effectively on many different levels is also a skill that will develop with training and, ultimately, experience as you need to be able to seamlessly move from discussing a case with a fellow veterinarian to then consulting with clients and explaining concepts in layman's terms. The next time you find yourself with a vet observe closely how they communicate with their client, both verbally and in terms of the body language they adopt. The benefit of this exercise is to identify what techniques work and to then adapt them and use them to fit your own consulting style – developing the 'art' of veterinary medicine if you will.

3. Outgoing and motivated – no one ever gets into vet school through someone else putting in the effort so it's important to be a self-starter and to possess the determination to carry through with things in order to make it as a vet. The applications process will be demanding, especially with so many pressures placed on you from all angles including school, the need to carry out placements and maintain your extra-curricular activities. It's not surprising then that most vet students and vets you meet will be fairly lively, outgoing people who have no problems deciding on a course of action and following it through to completion, even if the odds seem stacked against them and everything seems to be going wrong. This is important as not every case will be straightforward and follow the script – in fact, some are bloody nightmares that make you want to scream and go off to become a librarian instead (no offence to librarians!)

4. Confidence – as you will be trusted to examine people's animals and to then give your professional opinion on what is potentially wrong with them and what can be done to help them, it is important to have confidence in yourself. Having said this it is equally important to be able to recognise those gaps in your knowledge and/ or skills profile that are bound to exist and either seek to fill those deficits or refer your client and their animal to a more experienced or knowledgeable colleague. Seeking assistance, clarification or a second opinion is certainly not an admission of inadequacy but rather a sign that you are a sensible professional who is able to see past your own pride in order to seek the best treatment for your patient. This, in itself, takes a lot of confidence. It also takes huge amounts of confidence to approach people for placements and to then sit in front of admissions tutors whilst in interview. By reading this book you are even demonstrating your confidence in the fact that veterinary is the career for you.

5. Resourceful – vets are renowned for their ability to be able to think swiftly on their feet and react to unexpected scenarios effectively. You may find yourself in a clinical situation where you don't have the ideal, textbook equipment available and which requires you to think outside of the box and fashion a workable alternative – it happens far more than you would imagine and calls for people with the resourcefulness and logic to be able to adapt swiftly.

6. Forward-thinker – with preventative medicine becoming more and more important in veterinary, rather than just the traditional view of vets reacting to situations in an ER accident and emergency style, the ability to apply your training and knowledge to identify and implement long term strategies for animal health care is fast becoming vital. A lot of farm work, for example, revolves around discussing herd health and methods by which the farmer can effectively avoid having to call you out to treat sick animals – prevention truly is better than cure. This requires you, as the vet, to be able to identify potential gaps in a client's health planning and to advise them on how to keep their animals healthy. It is exactly the same principle in small animal medicine when we advise owners to neuter their new puppies or kittens in order to greatly reduce the risks of developing certain conditions such as tumours later in life, as well as the obvious reproductive benefits. Vets who just exist to treat sick cases as they walk through the door and are unable to think beyond this role are not really working as effectively as they could and are, in fact, somewhat detrimental to the animals whom they are charged to care for.

Graduate Student:
Harriet Baxter (2nd Year, Bristol Vet School)

It is not the end of the world if you don't get the A-levels that you want, even though it may seem it at the time. After all, you do have options and it is still possible to get into vet school! One of the options is to do a degree first before applying for veterinary science as a postgraduate. This was the route I chose. I got average A-levels but decided that rather than spend the time re-doing them I would take up my place at the University of Bristol where I had been offered a chance to read Anatomical Science with Veterinary Anatomy. I loved my first degree, I made some fantastic friends and although part of me wished that I was doing vet, the other half of me always knew that I would apply for it when I graduated. I found that there are many advantages to doing a first degree, one being time. Lie-ins and days off are not something that you're going to find plenty of whilst studying to become a vet! The other is the chance to make sure that vet is really what you want to do. You also get to experience the level of work that university expects of you, both as a vet student and a science undergraduate, which makes you much better prepared and realistic to what will be asked of you when you finally start the course.

At some of the universities, if you have completed a science based degree you may be eligible for direct entry into second year. This is available at Edinburgh, London and Liverpool. At Cambridge they will omit the third year of your prospective study so you can complete the course in 5 rather than 6 years.

There are a few catches with doing it this way which I must explain to you now:

1. Doing two degrees is expensive and unfortunately is the reason many people are unable to do it. At all the vet schools bar two you have to pay full second degree fees which are a lot. This year they are around £16,500 per annum and that's just for your academic

fees, never mind your rent and living, which you'll also have to pay. As I said though there are two exceptions : Nottingham and London, both of which offer places to postgraduates at the normal undergraduate fee of £3000 per annum, but understandably the places are much more competitive for this reason.

2. Time. The vet course is very demanding and you will find that you have lectures all day, everyday, so when friends are messing around in halls or at home you will be in lectures and practicals. Nearly all of the vet schools discourage students from working during the term time as a result of this. If students do need to work they recommend no more than 10 hours a week. Another difficulty is that you have less holiday than most other students due to the requirements for EMS (Extra Mural Studies) or work experience. In your first two years you are required to undertake 12 weeks of farm EMS in your holidays and in your last three years you are required to do 26 weeks of clinical EMS. This does eat into your holidays and therefore also leaves less time than you may otherwise have for earning money.

3. The level of work that will be expected of you during your first degree is not to be underestimated. For UK/EU graduate applicants, the vet schools will require you to have completed an Honours degree of class 2:1 or a 1st. They will usually expect the subject area of the Honours degree to be science based, but this is not compulsory at all universities. In the case of non-science graduates, chemistry and biology A-levels will be expected. Attaining a 2:1, let alone a first class degree, is not a walk in the park. It takes hard work and determination to complete it, especially if it's not in a subject that you are passionate about. But at the same time you will find it incredibly rewarding, you will be taught by people who are experts in their fields and by people who will give up a lot of time trying to pass on their knowledge and love of their subject. You will find this particularly in your third year when you have the opportunity to explore an area in great depths and become familiar with the most up to date research in that field.

I know that doing two degrees won't be for everyone but for those that can and want to, I would wholeheartedly recommend it. I have loved every second of both my degrees and I wouldn't have done it any other way. I'm now in my second year at Bristol finally reading Veterinary Science and although the work is tough and the hours long, vet students live by the ethos of work hard, play harder, and we at Bristol do just that! I won't say that the last five years has been a walk in the park because they haven't but what makes it all worthwhile is being asked what I do and being able to turn around and finally say, "I'm a Vet student".

Work Experience

Needless to say you must be hard-working as nobody got into vet school by sitting on their arse. In addition to getting top grades at school – which most mortals need to work to achieve – you also need to complete work experience placements, with a suggested minimum being experience of working on a dairy farm, sheep farm (eg at lambing), stables, pig farm, and time spent at a veterinary clinic shadowing both the vets and, very importantly, the nurses. Some of the vet schools offer suggestions on work experience but it's important to remember that the key thing with veterinary work placements is to demonstrate breadth of experience as opposed to length of time spent acquiring it. The vet schools want to see that you have really developed a good sense of what a potentially broad career veterinary is and the best way of doing this is to see what various aspects of the training and job could entail. This, naturally, also includes the potentially unsavoury aspects of working with animals. This includes, for example, experience of laboratories if you are able to secure such placements. It is important to be able to demonstrate that you really and truly have a good grasp on the realities of what training and working as a vet will be like. As such most schools would tend to choose a candidate who has spent a week at a small animal vets, one at a dairy farm and another at a laboratory over an otherwise identical candidate who has spent his/ her whole six week summer holiday shadowing the top equine soft tissue surgeon in the country. But just how do you secure these hallowed work placements? The answer is resourcefulness, enterprise, diplomacy and persistence. The initial step is working out what placements you want to do – aim to cover the basics first such as time spent on a dairy farm or at a veterinary clinic – and then identify who, in your area, or even outside your immediate area, could potentially help. I say also look outside your immediate area as it is widely acknowledged that it is getting tougher every day to secure good placements prior to getting into vet school so if you can widen your target base by also looking at placements near friends or family, who I am sure you could butter up and possibly stay with during work experience, then the greater your chances of not only getting some experience but also the more you will impress the selectors by your demonstration of lateral thinking, networking and determination. The best way to approach prospective placement providers is to find out who is in charge, for example by putting in a polite, enquiring telephone call or consulting the website, and then write a nice letter to this person introducing yourself, setting out your request briefly whilst all the while appreciating that, in actual fact, by offering you a placement they are really putting themselves out and making a big effort for you. It is this initial contact that can be the deal maker or breaker because if you fail to make a favourable impression in that first ten seconds then your letter/ email will be heading straight to the wire mesh filing cabinet on the floor! Simple things tend to put people off in written communication: poor letter construction, for example not having your address neatly typed in the top right hand corner, or not presenting the date professionally; miss-spelling the person's name or using the wrong title, for example using Mr when the addressee is in fact an esteemed Professor – a person's name is, after all, one of the single most precious things a person owns and to get it wrong in such a manner suggests a lack of care at the best and a complete lack of respect at the worst. Poor spelling is another no no, especially in the days of the spellchecker, as this, again, denotes a lack of care which the reader will unfairly or otherwise translate into other aspects of your character. The best way of ensuring a letter/ email asking for this kind of help is perfect is to ask someone like a teacher or friend to read it. It's probably better to ask someone older who is not a parent as they are more likely to give you an honest, objective opinion and will be able to guide you on how to improve it. So, letters are sent out – what now? In business or in the process of job-searching it is prudent to follow-up a letter with a courteous phone call a few days after it has been sent. This, first of all, demonstrates your professionalism, assuming of course you adopt a respectful and courteous phone manner, and secondly highlights your determination. They may be grateful for your call as they could have been so busy that they simply forgot about your fantastic letter but had been initially very impressed and had every intention of offering you a placement, in which case your call simply reminded them of who you are and what you are asking. It also enables them to put a human element to the name and, even if they are unable to help you themselves – if this is the case then graciously accept the fact and thank them for their time in considering your request – then they may be able to suggest an additional contact for you to try. This is often an excellent way of securing placements as it enables you to contact this person with a personal reference from someone they know and trust, which instantly makes you a viable option for consideration. Once a placement has been arranged then, first of all, enjoy yourself and try to learn as much from the experience as you can and, secondly, it's always a good idea to ask for a written reference from the placement provider as these can be taken with you to interviews. Also place any rejection letters you receive from placement providers in your portfolio as these all serve as evidence of the effort you went to find suitable work experience. The interviewers will appreciate the fact that it is getting harder to find good placements and that for every success you have there will be ten polite rejections. Once the basic types of placement have been covered then the next step is to try and secure at least one of those cracking Holy Grails of placements – the type that could prove to be your golden ticket into vet school. This is going to be the kind of placement that very few of your fellow applicants will have completed and could be anything. Chris, when he was fifteen, visited the Animal Health Trust in Newmarket with a friend who was taking their dog to the small animal centre, and made the decision to write a letter asking whether they could offer him a placement, despite knowing that they don't usually consider anyone under the age of sixteen. This initial letter, and the enthusiasm that it radiated for the specific provider, resulted in the arrangement of a fantastic two week summer placement, with time spent mainly at the small animal centre and some time spent at both the equine hospital, including the advanced imaging department, and the laboratories sited at the trust. There is no doubting the fact that being able to put the Animal Health Trust on his personal statement and presenting a glowing reference from them at his interviews helped secure offers from more than one vet school. Remember that inspiration for a great placement, or potential contacts and leads, can emerge from even the most unexpected source so always keep an open mind. If you are unable to arrange a particular type of placement then consider looking for experiences that are related. For example a friend of ours, Becky, was unable to secure a poultry placement so got involved in a school scheme called 'Living Eggs' whereby she took chicken eggs into schools, teaching children about chicken anatomy and instructing them on how to care for the eggs until they hatched. This lateral thinking and unique experience will impress selectors as much as any other placement.

Another good idea is to keep a brief diary of your work placements, noting any interesting cases, as this can be a useful reminder before the interviews, especially as there may be a relatively long gap between actually doing the placement and getting to talk about it with the admissions tutors. It is important to have at least a basic understanding of how farms and veterinary practices function and to appreciate exactly what the animals that may come under your care mean to the respective farmer or owner. A farmer would be expected to think of his livestock in a different manner than a pet owner so it is important to realise and appreciate this.

It is never too early to start researching the application process for veterinary school, with numerous cases existing of keen, enthusiastic would-be vets starting enquiries as early as age 12 and starting to gain practical experience by age 14. And why not? The earlier you start the greater the number and, most importantly, variety of practical experience you will be able to gain, as well as really demonstrating to the admissions tutors the extent of your commitment to veterinary as the career path for you. One of the most important and perhaps forgotten reasons behind any practical placement, both prior to application and whilst at vet school itself, is the importance of using the time and opportunity to work with and understand, and thus be able to recognise, healthy animals as it is only once you are comfortable with recognising health that you will be proficient at identifying disease. Talking of disease and health, another good reason for gaining as much experience as you are able is to check that you are both mentally and physically suited to a career in veterinary. Life as a vet can often require you to make a host of very difficult decisions, especially when considering those decisions that involve life or death. This can take its toll on vets and it is important to recognise in yourself the ability to be able to cope effectively with this type of pressure. It is a sad truth that the veterinary profession has one of the highest suicide rates amongst its members relative to others and this may have a large part to do with the fact that a lot is expected of us and, for some, the pressures can become too much. How do you cope with stress? Do you crumble in a heap at the first sign of a difficult situation or are you able to approach the same scenario with a cool head and level thought? If the latter then maybe you have what it takes to make tough decisions on an almost daily basis. The other health concern is allergies. How do you know you're not allergic to cows or cats unless you work with them? Answer is you can't possibly know and it's better to discover that you are actually unable to go within ten feet of a rabbit before you spend precious time and energy on applying to vet school than to turn up for that first practical at university and end up in hives having already committed to the course. It does happen. A friend of one of the authors managed to gain a place on the vet course with minimal work experience only to discover halfway through the first year that she was incredibly allergic to the vast majority of small domestic animals. The realisation that it was unreasonable to expect all her patients to be presented with a number one haircut was one of the reasons that prompted her to question her commitment and suitability for the veterinary profession. So much better to realise this early so as to focus your energies on an alternative and more suitable career. Having said this, allergies do not preclude you from working as a vet. After all, there are such things as anti-histamines!

So, the key points when it comes to work experience are:

1. Start as early as possible – decide what placements you want to do and write letters/ send emails

2. Variety is the magic word – better to spend one week each at three different placement types than to devote too much time and effort to one

3. Persistence – expect a lot of 'sorry, we are unable to help you' responses but don't be put off as all it takes are the occasional successes to make it all worthwhile.

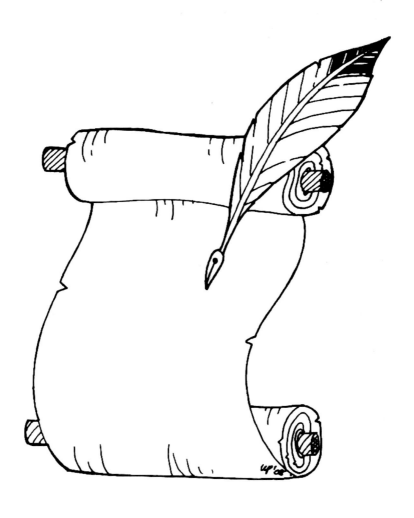

Vet School Applications

Admissions tutors have perhaps one of the most important jobs in the entire profession. Why? Because their decisions ultimately determine the future of the profession as the people they select to enter vet school are the same people who will go on to shape the industry. So what type of candidates are selectors being presented with? Whilst it is accurate to describe the profession as a varied one in terms of the number and type of different career paths open to veterinary graduates the same cannot really be said for the candidates being selected to enter vet school. At the moment anyway. The aim of the vet schools is to admit a good cross-section of the community but in recent years the type of student being selected has tended to be quite similar: predominantly female, white and from higher up the socioeconomic ladder. This may have a lot to do with the simple fact that this type of student is in the majority in terms of the type of student applying to study veterinary. Why then are we not seeing greater numbers of applications from students with less typical backgrounds? Is it because white, middle to upper class females are doing better at school than others? Perhaps. Is it because they have more opportunity to find and complete suitable work experience placements? Yes, quite probably, especially when it comes to finding good farming placements. Is it because veterinary as a career path just doesn't really appeal to non-traditional students? This is also likely to be true, with careers such as human medicine possibly appealing more. The veterinary profession is trying, rightly, to counter this trend whilst at the same time maintaining the very high standards asked of applicants. Why not just lower the entrance requirements, I hear you ask. Well, the reason vet schools demand students demonstrate such high levels of academic achievement is that this is still the most reliable measure of potential to be able to absorb, retain and recall vast amounts of information, an absolutely key skill for a vet. Weaker students, even if brilliant in all other respects, may start to find the intensity and amount of learning difficult. It is not in the interests of the student, the school or indeed the profession and owners to therefore relax this position. As mentioned, there are efforts to encourage students from less traditional backgrounds and with perhaps slightly weaker than required A-levels to consider veterinary science as a career option. The 'Walks of Life' campaign launched collectively by the RCVS, six of the seven UK vet schools, DEFRA, and DIUS is a project aimed at demonstrating how a veterinary degree can open doors into all sorts of work, ranging from industry to the more traditional practice route. It also highlights what you can expect from a career in veterinary science and the type of person who may thrive. For example, if you enjoy problem solving, would like to be your own boss, enjoy meeting both people and working with animals then veterinary could very well be the perfect career choice. It also draws attention to the fact that vet schools want to encourage applications from students who may come from more disadvantaged backgrounds and who may not have the right qualifications, by offering the opportunity to complete a foundation year before joining the main veterinary course. The option to study for an initial foundation year is – at the time of print – offered by London, Liverpool and Bristol, with Nottingham seeking to widen access by offering a six year course designed for high-achieving students with non-science backgrounds. If you are unsuccessful in your applications to veterinary school but continue to harbour a burning desire to work with animals then it's important to realise that there are a plethora of animal-related areas that you could work in, ranging from zoology and conservation to veterinary nursing or behaviour and welfare. The options really are vast. More information on the 'Walks of Life' campaign can be found on the website (www.walksoflife.org.uk) and on the YouTube page (www.youtube.com/vetcareers), where a range of interesting veterinary career related videos can be viewed.

We have already touched upon the subject of what proportion of vet school places go to which students, with the vast majority of them being offered to school leavers/ Gap Year students and the remainder being made available to overseas and graduate students. In terms of the attributes that admissions tutors are looking for we covered a large proportion of these in the previous chapter. One of the main things tutors want to see, however, is motivation. Those people who say grades are not important at this stage are misleading you however, as although A-level grades will not be available yet to tutors they will have your GCSE and possibly AS results to hand. The vet schools will all have minimum requirements for GCSE grades, with AS levels not so important, and so if you fail to demonstrate evidence of good grades at GCSE, especially in the core subjects of science, maths and English then chances are that you might not make it past the initial screening process. If you do make it this far then how do you peak the tutor's interest enough to be called for interview? Well, as said before, they want to see evidence of motivation: what placements you have done, whether you have simply ticked the boxes in terms of gaining the minimum amount of and type of placement, or whether you have pushed beyond the box by going that extra mile and completing some unique placement. They will also want to see evidence of your extracurricular activities. Some advisors will try and tell you to exaggerate your interests by, for example, saying you run when all you really do is leg it for the bus every morning because you're late. Our advice is don't bullshit. The tutors have seen and heard it all before and can spot a chancer a mile off. If you have genuine interests and hobbies then by all means enthuse about them on your application but the minute you stretch the truth you are leaving yourself wide open to potential embarrassment when you're asked about them in more detail at interview. We wouldn't claim to be world class jazz guitarists if we weren't as chances are one of your interviewers will be an enthusiast and ask you about it – after all, interviewers love to talk about things they are really interested in rather than the dry admissions gumph that will make up the bulk of most interviews, and will be at best disappointed and at worst go right off you if they suspect you're a liar. There will be more on maximising the impact of your personal statement in a later chapter.

Ok, so you have the predicted grades and a stack of great GCSEs as well as a range of great work experience placements, but when do you actually submit your application to the vet schools and, more importantly, how do you go about doing so? All prospective vet students have to submit their applications through UCAS (Universities and Colleges Application Service), the agency that deals with all university applications, by no later than the 15th October. The first thing you will need to decide is which of the seven UK vet schools you wish to apply to, as current rules permit you to apply to a maximum of four schools, with the remaining one choice on your UCAS form reserved for you to either consider putting down an 'insurance course' in case you are unsuccessful in your applications to vet school or to leave blank. The decision over whether to put down any non-veterinary courses, such as biochemistry or zoology, is a personal one and depends on whether you could feasibly see yourself doing another course should you not be offered a place at veterinary school. Some people worry that if they do put down anything other than veterinary on their applications then the schools will see this and it will cast doubt in their minds over your commitment to veterinary and thus offer them an excuse to reject you in favour of more committed candidates. This is not the case, especially as none of the schools can see who else or what else you have applied for, although they can see if you've put down four or five choices but not the detail. Some people make the decision not to put down an insurance course and then if they are unsuccessful with their application but then plan to reapply the following year they may then hedge their applications by including an insurance course. It really is a personal choice and depends on whether you would be happy to study a non-vet course first and then possibly apply to vet school as a graduate or take a chance and reapply the next year. The choice of vet schools you put on your application is, again, a very personal matter and all we can do is offer some insight into what each of the vet schools is like and what they offer in terms of course specifics. The best way of really getting the measure of each of the schools and whether you would be happy both studying and living there is to visit the university, either on one of the official open days, of which there are normally several each year, or independently. University prospectuses, websites and individual course literature also offer a valuable source of information on what the culture of the individual school is. Another great potential source of honest, reliable information on what each course and university is like is to speak to current, or recently graduated students. These people will be able to give you the type of insight that no official open day or course brochure could ever offer and we urge you to try and find someone to talk to – in fact, considering the fact that we are somehow connected to everyone by approximately six people (degrees of separation) it is worth betting that you will know someone who knows someone else who may then know someone who is either at vet school or who, themselves, knows someone else you could speak to. If you really are serious about improving your chances of gaining a place at vet school then you will be fully prepared to speak to anyone and everyone to gather information to guide your application decisions. And remember that vet students don't bite. Well, not hard anyway. You really need to ask yourself what kind of experience you want from your time at vet school, which will be at least five years in length. For example, if you really don't like big cities and prefer a quieter pace of life then perhaps London isn't the ideal first choice whereas Cambridge may offer a better choice. Do you want to stay relatively close to home or are not bothered if it takes eight hours to go home during holidays? Is there a particular extra-curricular activity that you enjoy doing that might dictate where in the country you would wish to apply? For example, if you're a super-keen surfer who loves spending their time catching waves in Cornwall then an application to Bristol would make more sense than omitting it in favour of land-locked Nottingham. Also, the style of university and the degree of integration with the rest of the university are both factors which may influence your decision. London, for example, is a stand-alone institution where, unless you live in shared halls for the first year, it is unlikely that you will mix much with non-veterinary students. This is in contrast to a university like Bristol or Edinburgh where the vet school, certainly for the initial pre-clinical years of the course, are part of the main university and so there is far more opportunity to integrate with students from other subjects. Cambridge, as ever, is unique in this respect due to the college based nature of the education provided. You will, for the duration of your time at Cambridge, be a member of a specific college, physically living in for at least your fresher year. As such you will live, dine, socialise and possibly spend time studying with students from a variety of different subjects. This can be a really rewarding experience and allow you make great, potentially lifelong, friends and contacts from a range of different backgrounds and disciplines.

In terms of the chances of success in applying to vet school, there are approximately 2.5 applicants to each place – much better odds than the inflated figures of 65 to 1 that I am sure you have heard banded about. As such, as long as you satisfy the academic requirements, complete a good range of work experience and come across well in your UCAS statement then chances are very high that you will be called for the all important interview. We will discuss the interview and methods of maximising your chances of performing well in them a little later in the book.

What if you don't manage to get a place at vet school? Given the fact that it is still an extremely competitive course with very stringent entrance requirements there is a chance that you may not be offered a place and that is something you do need to be realistic about and thus have a contingency plan for. The options are varied. You could always reapply the following year, maybe using the year before to increase the quality and quantity of your experience or retake some exams if your grades were lower than you were hoping for. Alternatively, you could opt to exercise your insurance option and go to university to study a non-veterinary subject with the aim of either following an alternative career path, for example scientific research and development, or apply to veterinary as a graduate in a few years. There is, of course, the option of applying to study veterinary outside of the UK, which is maybe an option that you hadn't really considered. The UK, after all, isn't the only country in the world that has vet schools. Europe, the USA, Australia and New Zealand are all credible options for applying to. St Georges in the Caribbean is another option, with the prospect of spending your final year attached to one of the AVMA-accredited (American Veterinary Medical Association) UK vet schools in order to complete your clinical stage of training. Obviously all of the overseas schools are different in terms of their course structure, teaching styles and overall culture and it is beyond the scope of this book to look at them all in detail. The main thing to bear in mind, however, when and if considering applying to study outside of the UK is that, with the possible rare exception, you will not be automatically awarded MRCVS (membership of the Royal College of Veterinary Surgeons) status upon graduation and will need to sit a separate set of exams to be eligible to work in the UK as a vet, with no guarantee that you will even pass these. It is worth highlighting also that at the time of publication candidates are only permitted three attempts at sitting the MRCVS exams. As such there is a chance that in spite of graduating as a vet in the country in which you study you may not be able to practice in the UK. The other consideration is the cost as you will not be considered a home student but rather an overseas student and as such will likely be expected to pay the relevant fees, which as for overseas studying in the UK are considerably higher than home candidates. Again, this is something that will vary depending on which school you apply to but needs to be thought about, especially as most universities will want to see some kind of proof that you are going to be able to pay. Visas, language and travel and living expenses are also additional factors that must be considered in applying to schools outside of the UK. Our advice, if you are seriously considering this as an option, is to start your research early and really be clear on all the specifics of the application process and costs.

Grades

These are, of course, very important with the average minimum requirement being AAB at A-level, of which at least one has to be chemistry. This often surprises candidates who, understandably, are under the impression that biology would be the more important subject for fairly obvious reasons. The truth is, however, that a lot of veterinary science relies upon a good basic grasp of biochemistry and pharmacology and so understanding chemistry is vital. You will be taught the specifics of veterinary anatomy and physiology on the course so biology is, in some respects, covered again whilst at vet school with the perk that there is no plant biology to worry about! It used to be the case that to stand the best chance of getting into vet school you needed to have at least three sciences at A-level, with some candidates opting to study perhaps an additional science or supplement their core science grades with a non-science subject such as English. This stance has changed somewhat with a lot of the schools accepting non-science subjects more readily than before. Having said this, most vet schools will still look for candidates to offer at least two sciences at A-level, or the equivalent, although in some cases they may be open to considering an exceptional candidate with chemistry and other non-science subjects. The reason for relaxing this traditional approach to viewing A-level grades is likely due to the vet schools' desire to broaden access to veterinary as a career and encourage fresh thinking and ideas. However, it must be born in mind that if you do apply to study vet science and study only chemistry at A-level then expect to be questioned as to why you didn't consider another science to be a suitable subject, especially biology. Remember that the admissions tutors want to see evidence that you have really thought about your career choice and that you haven't just selected veterinary on a whim. It is a reasonable question to ask and one which you should expect to be asked so if you are in this position then have a convincing argument prepared. As mentioned previously, some of the vet schools have schemes in place to widen participation in their course by offering foundation years for those students who have either just fallen short of the required grades but are otherwise considered excellent candidates and those candidates with no real scientific background but who wish to train as a vet.

Obviously we appreciate that the vast majority of students applying won't have sat their final A-levels at the time of application and will be using their GCSE and AS level results as the base of their applications. As such, it is important to have good grades in both with predicted grades in your A-levels also taken into account. You may be asked which AS levels you are sitting at full A-level and your reasons for this decision. Many students ask us what they should do in regard to their AS levels – are they better to study more subjects to achieve more A-levels or drop some in order to focus their energies on fewer subjects thus increasing the chances of achieving high grades. The first thing to say is that this is a very personal decision and depends on many factors. For a start ask yourself whether you will have the time and dedication to achieve high grades in, for example, five subjects or whether you will potentially be stretching yourself too thin. Also, will studying for more subjects give you less time to focus on extra-curricular activities and work experience? Unless you are sure that you can cope with the extra work and pressure our advice would be to seriously consider focusing on just three or four subjects at A-level and really making sure that you achieve top grades in them. Better to come away with two As and a B than to get five Bs and miss out on a place at vet school because the conditional offer you received was for AAB. The other thing to remember is that by studying more than three subjects you may even end up making life more difficult for yourself by attracting conditional offers that include more than three subjects. For example, we know of candidates who have been studying four A-levels and thus received conditional offers of AABB or something similar –

additional pressure when most schools will be more than satisfied with three good A-levels.

A lot of students also ask about resits and what the implications are for their application. It is our understanding that the schools do not get any notification of how many times you have resat a module and so if you feel you need to bump up your grade by devoting time to a resit then go for it. However, ask yourself whether this would really be the best use of your time and whether you could instead focus on working harder for the next module and ace that. The danger is that by focusing precious time on revising for resits you may inadvertently increase the risk of performing below potential at your upcoming exams. If you get poorer grades than expected come final results day and decide to opt for a gap year in which to resit your A-levels, be mindful of the fact that you may be expected to re-take full subjects and not allowed to just sit individual modules to bump up your original grades. Most of the vet schools would also be likely to expect you to achieve at least three grade As if you have had an extra year in which to work for them.

"I don't do A-levels – what about me?!" You may be one of the increasing number of students who rather than studying for A-levels are sitting, or have already sat, an International Baccalaureate or, if studying in Scotland, have Highers and Advanced Highers. What advice do we have for you? We have compiled a table summarising each of the vet schools' minimum requirements for various examination results, correct at the time of publication. If in doubt, however, it is always a good idea to check out each vet school's website or contact their admissions department to clarify requirements.

Cambridge Applications

The Cambridge veterinary intake is the smallest of all the UK vet schools, with numbers for 2008 intake capped at 65 places. The course is six years in length, and includes a year of intercalation which is undertaken as the third year. The end of the third year signals the end of the first Tripos and it is at this point that students are awarded a BA. Applications are made to individual colleges, with applicants able to either submit an application to a specific college or an open application whereby a candidate will be randomly allocated to a college by a computer system. Cambridge candidates are required to sit the BMAT test and to have achieved, or be predicted to achieve, a minimum of AAA at A-level. If you are applying with qualifications other than A-levels you are encouraged to check specific requirements with the college to which you are applying. Cambridge has a general preference for applicants applying with three sciences/ maths at A-level, with at least one needing to be chemistry.

Cambridge produce an online leaflet summarising the main points of their application process for veterinary medicine and we encourage you to consult this resource for further information.

Academic course requirements – the following table summarises the minimum academic requirements of the UK vet schools. It is only intended as a guide and candidates are urged to consult the relevant website of the individual schools, as requirements are always subject to change.

	London	Bristol	Cambridge	Glasgow	Edinburgh	Liverpool	Nottingham
A-Level/A2	3 subjects, including Biology & Chemistry. Standard offer of AAB.	AAB to include Chem, Biology & another academic subject	AAA to include Chemistry and Biology, Physics or Maths	AAB to include Chemistry, Biology & another academic subject	3 subjects (AAB), including Chemistry (A), Biology & either Maths or Physics	21 units – normally 3 A2 plus an AS. 2 sciences, including Biology. Standard offer AAB	AAB to include Chemistry & Biology (both at A)
GCSE	5 subjects (Double Science or Biology & Chemistry at grade A), English, Maths and Physics at grade B or above	Widespread good grades, including Chemistry, Biology, Physics (or Double Science), English & Maths	Grade A, B or C in Physics, Biology (or Double Science) & Maths			Good range. Grade B in Maths, English, Physics (or Double Science, including Physics)	5 grade As, including Chemistry, Biology & Physics (or Double Science). Minimum grade B in Maths & English

Ordinary/Standard	Irish:	Advanced Highers	Highers	Scot:	IB
Physics (minimum grade B)		Pass Advanced Highers in Biology & Chemistry (AA-BB)	5 Highers, including Biology, Chemistry & Physics (AAAAB)		Biology, Chemistry & one other subject (Higher) – offers normally Grades 7, 6, 6, and an acceptable qualification in Physics, Maths & English
		Chemistry & Biology (AA-AB)	AAABB or higher		35 points or higher. Chemistry & Biology, and other subjects (Higher) – Grades of 6, 6, 6 required in all
		Chemistry & Biology (BB-BB)	AAABB or higher, including Chemistry (A), Biology & Physics or Maths		36 points or higher. Chemistry & Biology at Grade 6 or 7 and Maths or Physics at Grade 5
		Chemistry & one other science (BB)	5 Highers, including Chemistry & two of Biology, Maths, Physics (AAABB)		36 points or higher. Chemistry, Biology and Maths or Physics (Higher). Grades of 6, 6, 6 required in all subjects.
		Equates with A-level so standard offer is AAB	Good range of Highers – mainly As.		3 subjects (Higher), including Chemistry & Biology. Total score 38 or higher. Grades of 6, 7 or higher specified.
Minimum of grade B in Physics, Maths & English		AA in Chemistry & Biology	Minimum grade B in Physics, Maths & English		38 points or higher. Chemistry & Biology, Grades 6 & 7.

Higher/ Honours	AAAABB including Biology & Chemistry	Requirements on website.			5 subjects, including Chemistry (A), Biology & Maths or Physics (AA), two other major subjects (BB)	6 subjects, including Chemistry & Biology, and Maths or Physics. Standard offer is 4As, 2Bs	6 subjects, including all sciences. 5 grade As required, including all sciences

For requirements to study Veterinary at Dublin, candidates are directed to the university's website (http://www.ucd.ie/vetmed/)

It is worth noting that depending on how well you do at interview and your specific background, universities may decide to make you an offer which is lower than the standard stated in their prospectuses.

BMAT

The BioMedical Admissions Test is a two hour pen and paper assessment comprising three distinct sections and is, at the time of publication, required by both the Royal Veterinary College and Cambridge University veterinary courses. The three sections of the test are:

Section 1: Aptitude and Skills – 60 minutes, 35 multiple-choice questions. This section tests generic skills in problem solving, understanding argument and data analysis and inference.

Section 2: Scientific Knowledge and Applications – 30 minutes, 27 multiple-choice or short answer questions. Scientific knowledge normally taught in non-specialist school science and maths courses is tested by this section, up to and including National Curriculum Stage 4 higher double science and maths. No calculators are allowed to be used in this assessment.

Section 3: Writing Task – 30 minutes, 1 essay question from a choice of 3. This tests candidates' ability to select, develop and organise ideas and communicate them in writing in a concise and effective way. The questions often take the form of a statement which candidates are then invited to interpret and analyse.

All sections are sat during the same 2 hour paper and candidates need to apply to sit the test through a dedicated test centre, with most colleges registered with Cambridge Assessment, the company which produces and marks them. The test is usually staged in November, with results made available in December of the same year. Candidates' results are automatically forwarded to those institutions on students' UCAS application that require the BMAT, which in the case of veterinary is both the Royal Veterinary College (London) and Cambridge. For costs of sitting the BMAT candidates are encouraged to refer to the BMAT website (*www.admissionstests.cambridgeassessment.org.uk/adt/bmat*), where sample papers and advice are also made available. The BMAT is not an assessment that can be 'crammed' for although some familiarisation with the paper format and style can help improve your chances of scoring well.
However, no company offering 'tutoring' or practice tests have any additional insight into how the BMAT test works and candidates are better off downloading example papers from the website and referring to guides made available.

Nottingham Application Process

There are four phases to the application process to gain a place at Nottingham. These phases are:

1. **Phase 1** – Further information collection (via online questionnaire)
   After submitting the UCAS form candidates are invited to complete an online questionnaire providing additional information and giving examples and evidence of the following candidate attributes:
   a. Communication and Motor Skills, including animal handling skills
   b. Personal attributes and attitudes, including your motivation for seeking a career in veterinary and examples of effective teamwork

    c.   Insight into Veterinary as a career, including evidence of work experience and an understanding and appreciation of positive and negative aspects of a career as a vet

    d.   Sound reasons for wanting to study veterinary

2. **Phase 2** – Academic Review

This phase aims to examine a candidate's academic record in order to assess their level of knowledge, scholastic ability and basic numeracy and literacy.

3. **Phase 3** - Non-Academic Personal Qualities Review

Personal statements, referee reports and Phase 1 information are reviewed to assess personal attributes, personality and communication skills that are deemed important. At this stage a short-list of candidates is prepared.

4. **Phase 4** – Interview, Practical and Team working assessment

Interviews are conducted by two people and normally last about twenty minutes. They may also involve the use of live animals. The Practical assessment also lasts twenty minutes and involves the handling of animal material and use of clinical information. The assessment is not a test of knowledge but rather of analytical and observational skills as well as enthusiasm. The team working assessment is conducted in groups and is a test of a candidate's ability to work within a group.

Georgina Hirst BVetMed
MRCVS

Georgina graduated from the RVC and is currently in equine practice. Travels after graduation took her from the harsh living of Morocco to the grandeur of Dubai.

My name is Georgina Hirst and I graduated from the Royal Veterinary College in July 2007. The five weeks of revision leading up to finals were absolute hell but the long hours and hard work throughout the five years were all made worthwhile when graduation day finally arrived. My dreams of becoming a vet had finally come true and I had a qualification that would stay with me for the rest of my life. I loved my time at university and I made some amazing friends.

Entering the real world was a sudden realisation - making decisions on peoples' beloved animals was quite a scary prospect. Unlike my fellow peers who started work almost straight away, I wanted to delay entering the real world. I wanted to travel and see some of the world and experience different cultures!

My first stop was Morocco where I spent a month working as a volunteer for a very worthy horse charity called SPANA. My days were spent treating sick and injured mules and donkeys. The cases we dealt with were very varied with anything from routine worming, teeth and foot care, to dealing with colics, fractures, wounds and rabies. How I managed to get bitten by a one eyed mule I will never know! It was an amazing experience, seeing a country for what it is, working alongside the locals, and realising how much good you can do with minimal resources. Some of the cases I saw were heart-breaking, but seeing how much some of the owners cared about their animal, even though they could hardly feed themselves, was very moving.

On returning from Morocco I then went to Dubai to undertake a 6-month internship at the impressive Dubai Equine Hospital in the UAE where I was lucky enough to work with some top clinicians in their relevant fields, practising best medicine, as money wasn't an object. I had the enviable opportunity to work with some of the most valuable racehorses and endurance horses in the world. I worked long, unsociable hours and my days were spent caring for inpatients, and working up any emergencies that came in, as well as assisting with surgeries and diagnostic imaging. We also spent time working with the track vets at the races at Nad al Sheba and also attended the endurance races in the desert where we would work in the treatment tent, dealing with any metabolically compromised horses. The caseload was very varied dealing with a high medical caseload, lots of foals and colics. It was an amazing experience. Dubai was a great place to spend the winter - everyday you would wake up knowing it would be hot and sunny! Spending my few days off on the beach and enjoying the exclusive lifestyle of Dubai was amazing.

Being a vet has enabled me to travel and experience the culture of different countries, as well as learning from some well-respected clinicians. I wont deny its been hard work, and I have experienced sleep deprivation to the extreme, but that goes with the nature of the job, and I will never regret a moment of it. The opportunities are out there - you just have to go grab them!

I'm now working in a large equine practice in Leicestershire, but where I will go next – who knows?! Being able to do a job I love, and experience the world at the same time is an amazing privilege.

UCAS Form

The UCAS form is the gatekeeper to an interview and thus the offer of a place at vet school. As such it is imperative that you get this part of the process right. The first thing to find out is when the deadline for applications to UCAS is, with last year's deadline for medicine, dentistry, veterinary and all courses at both Oxford and Cambridge being 15th October. A useful exercise is to prepare an agenda/ timetable so that you can plan the timing of your application and see at a glance when you need to have everything completed by. The earlier you get the UCAS form completed then the more time you will have to review and refine your application. The UCAS website (www.ucas.ac.uk) is an excellent resource not only in terms of submitting your final application and tracking its progress but also in terms of the wealth of useful tools on the site for helping you to plan your applications effectively – definitely worth a look at very early on in the year.

There are several sections to the UCAS form, all of which is now completed and submitted online through their website. If you do not have access to the internet then we advise that you contact UCAS as soon as possible to discuss alternative methods of submitting your application. Each candidate needs to complete six sections as part of their application:

1. Personal details

2. Additional information (UK applicants only)

3. Course and university choices – remember that you can only choose up to a maximum of four veterinary courses, and that each university will not be able to see who else you have applied to

4. Education details, including courses taken and currently being studied, and results both achieved and pending

5. Employment

6. Personal statement – this is otherwise referred to as Section 10 and will be discussed in more detail later.

Once you have completed your sections of the application and are happy with what you have included, meaning that there is nothing in it that you may wish to change at a later date, then you will need to send your application and the fee (£17 if applying to two or more courses/ £7 if applying to just a single course – 2008 price) to the person writing your reference, who will complete this section of the application and then submit the completed application to UCAS. It is advisable that referees write their references once they have been able to read your personal statement, thus enabling them to supplement and support your statement as opposed to either repeating information or, more damagingly, contradicting information that you have put in your statement. As such it is clear why candidates are encouraged to complete their applications early and submit them to their referees long before the UCAS deadline. The type of information that referees will typically give in their statements include your predicted grades, their assessment of your suitability to train for a particular profession – so if the person who writes your reference knows you like torturing frogs outside of school, don't expect them to commend you to the universities as a great candidate to study veterinary! They will also typically comment on your performance in specific subjects/ exams if it is deemed that such additional information would support or strengthen your application. Information on any factors that might have or may in the future be expected to affect your academic performance could also be included as might information about any special requirements or special needs you may have, but only with your permission. Referees may also include details of any commitments (eg January assessments) which could prevent you from attending interviews on that specific date. It is worth remembering that under the Data Protection Act you are legally entitled to ask UCAS for a copy of any references or other personal information they hold on you. The aim of the referee, at the end of the day, will be to support and enhance your application by painting you in the best possible light. Our advice is to find out who will be likely to write your reference and make sure they know who you are – for all the right reasons! If you've had any run-in with this particular member of staff before then try to put all this behind you and work on getting in their good books long in advance of the application deadline – some may call it creeping, we just call it smart career engineering.

Another vitally important point to make on UCAS applications is to urge you to check and recheck that you use the correct course code when completing this section of the application. For example, veterinary at Liverpool is referred to as Veterinary Science whilst at London it is called Veterinary Medicine. London has another veterinary course called Bioveterinary Science, a three year degree course which will not enable you to work as a vet. It is easy to get confused and look up the wrong code to include on your form. You don't want the shock and disappointment of being called for interview for a course that sounds like the true vet course when you had actually wanted to apply for the vet course itself. So check, check and check again. We have created a table summarising the veterinary courses offered at each university, including the relevant UCAS course codes, which can be found in the appendix.

Once you have researched the courses and been to open days and generally have a good idea which four vet schools you want to apply to you'll be ready to fill out the form. Each year similar queries are asked so we feel it prudent to try and answer most of them now, before you are faced with issues during your application:

a) *How many courses should I include on my application?*
The answer is as many as you like, bearing in mind that you can apply to a maximum of four veterinary courses. As such you can include just one 'insurance' course in case you are unsuccessful in gaining a place at a vet school. Although each university will not be able to see which other universities you have applied to it is the authors' understanding that an individual university will be able to see if you have applied to two courses offered by that institution. For example, if you apply to Bristol to study veterinary and then also put down, as one of your 'insurance' courses, biochemistry at Bristol then the admissions tutor will be able to see this and will ask you about this should you be called for interview. Some students may not wish to run the risk of their commitment to veterinary science being called into question in this way by either opting not to include an insurance course on their

application or by choosing universities separate to those offering the veterinary courses to which they have applied.

b) *Which alternative course should I choose?*

Again, the answer to this is a very personal one and depends largely on where your interests lay outside of veterinary medicine. Obviously if your intention is to go on and apply to veterinary as a graduate following an initial degree then it would be fairly foolish to choose to study something that wasn't even vaguely scientific, unless you plan to enter one of the foundation year courses designed for gifted, non-science candidates. The main reason for this is that veterinary is ultimately a science, although as you will very quickly learn there is a fair amount of 'art' to the subject as well. If, however, you have no intention of pursuing veterinary as a career option should you be unsuccessful in your initial application then I guess you'd be better off choosing something that you are really interested in doing, whatever that may be. However, there are a few caveats to mention. First, if this sounds like a description of your attitude towards veterinary then perhaps you need to ask yourself whether you are really and truly committed to it as a career because unless your heart is in it 100% you will find the preparation, applications and the course itself incredibly tough. So, if you're thinking that if you don't make it into vet school this year then perhaps you'd like to go and study economics instead we suggest you take a long hard look at yourself and ask whether your future really lies in the city – as in City of London – as opposed to life dealing with animals. Secondly, do not under any circumstances put down either human medicine or dentistry as your insurance course. You will be shot down in flames and, again, you need to ask yourself which career you are really committed to: a veterinary healthcare career or one treating humans? Lots of courses would be excellent boards from which to kick off a veterinary career, with subjects such as anatomy, biology and zoology having obvious crossovers with veterinary science. The key point to make about choosing a science degree as an insurance course is that it will provide you with the kind of scientific training and grounding that will mean that your transition into life as a vet student will be seamless. You will be able to hit the ground running as you're already skilled in how to make good scientific notes in lectures, how to research, write and present great scientific essays, and how to design, execute and analyse original research. The point is that such a first degree will mean you enter the vet course as a scientist and will be able to fly from day one.

c) *Is transfer possible from another course?*
Although it has happened it is safe, and indeed sensible, not to bank on being able to take this route as it is one that is rarely available. The best advice if you do find yourself doing another non-veterinary course but really desperately want to get onto a vet course is to ring the admissions tutors before, during and up to a few weeks after fresher week. This is, however, unlikely to be successful.

d) *Should I apply for deferred entry/ take a Gap Year?*
Gap Years are becoming increasingly popular and for good reason. There is a strong case for encouraging students to consider taking a break from academia prior to starting university and if used effectively it can end up being one of the best years of your life and really change you for the better. Most students would agree that a Gap Year teaches them to become independent and provides a welcome respite from the rigours of school life that you will have been part of for so many years so far, and which you are going to be part of for at least the next five years. Some people choose to do the 'traditional' thing of travelling whilst others use the year to earn much needed money to ease the financial burden at university. Whatever you decide to do the main point to make is that you should have a purpose, especially if you're planning on applying to vet school for a deferred place. So, will you use the year to earn money, or gain further experience with animals, or just aim to broaden your horizons and outlook on life by travelling to far flung parts of the world. As long as you have a basic plan that doesn't boil down to spending a year sitting around in your pants perfecting your score in Guitar Hero then you will be fine. You should check, however, with the individual universities in order to ascertain their stance towards gap years, as some look upon them more favourably than others. Chris actually applied for his place to start straight after A-levels but upon receiving his grades decided that a gap year would be a really good idea and a chance to take stock and recharge before the commitment and hard work of five more years in

education. As such, he rang his university to discuss the possibility of deferring his place for a year, fully expecting to be told that if he didn't attend that year then his place would be lost, and was pleasantly surprised when they okayed the idea. Chris gave them a rough idea of what he planned to do during the year, including earning some money and gaining some interesting work experience. In the end, however, he worked in the UK for six months and then travelled to New Zealand for six months on a working holiday, with no animal-based activity undertaken for the entire year! "It was by far and away the best year of my life, and I can truly say that I eventually went to university a far more confident and prepared person than I would have been straight from school." The beauty of a gap year as well is that it really is a blank canvas with the potential to do literally anything open to you, which can be incredibly refreshing when considering that the next five or more years of your life are going to be fairly intense and planned out for you. Some people argue that it is better to take a gap year after university, but we would counter this by arguing that most people will be so worried and financially crippled by student debt that their main objective, after a good break naturally, is to get a job and start earning some much needed cash. Also, there is a lot to say for wanting to get out there into practice fairly soon after graduating to, if anything, consolidate those key 'day one' skills you have. It's probably far harder to enter the veterinary job market as a fresh faced, inexperienced new graduate a year after leaving university, especially as you will find yourself competing with the new vets graduating that year. It's probably better in this case to plan to work for a year or two, earn some money and develop as a good first opinion vet and then plan to take some time out to travel.

d) What if I don't make the grades asked of me by my first choice university?

If you find yourself in this position come results day then the first thing to remember is not to panic. Getting on the phone as soon as possible to your university's admissions tutor is the aim of the game as you may be pleasantly surprised to learn that you impressed the interviewers so much that they want you to still have the place despite missing out on the grades marginally. Even if they are unable to allow you to keep the place they may be able to offer you some very useful advice.

e) **What if I do better than my predicted grades but I don't have a place at vet school?**

First of all, congratulations – you must be well chuffed! Again, ring the university admissions tutors as soon as possible as it happens that a handful of offers are changed from rejections to unconditional offers for the following year based on students doing better than predicted. The main point in both of the previous cases is that you really need to be talking to someone in admissions at the universities, and as soon as possible the better. And remember, gaining a place at vet school is like much else in life: if you don't ask, you won't get!

Section 10: Personal Statement

This is one of the most important documents you will write in the process of your applications and is definitely worth spending time getting it spot-on. It is effectively a bid proposal: you are bidding to accept a much coveted place at vet school and selling yourself to the universities. As you only have a finite amount of space in which to type you will need to be good at conveying all the essential information about yourself in as succinct and effective a manner as possible. The first step in this process is to decide what information you are going to include and how you are going to organise it. There is certain key information that will definitely need to be covered and it is essential to present this clearly so that busy, overstressed admissions tutors can scan your statement easily and see at a glance whether you are a good candidate for the 'interview' pile. Put yourself in their shoes, or indeed the shoes of anyone 'recruiting' for a particularly popular job: there, in front of you lay hundreds (literally!) of fairly identical applications and you have a finite amount of time to read through them and select those candidates you think should be interviewed. Obviously you want to get home at some point and so will be in efficient scanning mode, a technique you have perfected over years of selecting the vets of the future. Imagine your frustration at having to plough through heavy block of prose after heavy block when all of a sudden, to your surprise and delight there sits a god-send of a personal statement which is written in comfortably sized, easily read font, is organised well, possibly with the use of carefully selected sub-titles, and which presents you and all your attributes and achievements swiftly and effectively. You know for a fact that you'd be so impressed by this kind of application that it would instantly go onto the 'interview' pile and put a smile on your face. Be that applicant. Have that effect. But how? Well, read on.

One important thing to remember when writing your statement is although we can offer advice and tips on how to strengthen your statement it is ultimately yours and no-one else's. As such go with your gut a lot of the time regards the style of writing – it has to be personal especially if you are to sit and chat about it with the interviewers. The other thing to note is that writing a 'medical' personal statement is completely different to writing one for any other course. This may mean that your careers advisor or head of year will not actually know what is specifically required. If your school is not used to sending students to veterinary school then try to find a student or lecturer at one of the universities to read your statement and comment on it.

Sections to include:

a) *Why do you want to be a vet?*
This is the most obvious question that anybody could ask you yet is one that is easy to answer poorly. It is not sufficient to say "I have always wanted to be a vet," or to claim that you "love animals." Chances are everyone else has and does. What the admissions tutors want to see is that you understand what it is that's unique about a career in veterinary medicine as opposed to a career in human medicine or any other job working with animals, of which there are dozens. It's perfectly reasonable to say that you have, for many years, harboured a desire to effectively use your skills to help animals in need wherever possible and that veterinary medicine offers the perfect opportunity for you to achieve this. This statement communicates your heartfelt desire to help animals and makes it clear that you are realistic in your expectations by including the words "wherever possible." This is important as it shows that you appreciate that it is not always possible, either due to financial constraints or another

reason, to do everything possible to help an animal in need. Vets are not miracle workers after all and nor are we afforded the luxury of unlimited clinical freedom over all of our patients. Animals come with owners and owners come with wallets which can be accessed to incredibly varying degrees. The crux of the matter is that sometimes you may be certain that a particular test or treatment could greatly enhance the quality of life for an animal but if that patient is either not insured, the insurance won't pay or the owners are unable or unwilling to pay and proceed then there is little you can do to help that animal further. It is frustrating and both of us have seen cases where this applies but it is the harsh truth of private veterinary medicine and it is one that as a vet student and future vet you need to accept and recognise. The vet schools will treat your application with the respect it duly deserves if you are able to convey this mature appreciation of the limitations of modern veterinary practice succinctly and early in your statement. They also want to see that you have recognised what it takes to be a good vet, rather than just deciding that because you like stroking cats a career in veterinary is perfectly suited to you and vice versa. So, acknowledging the link between being a scientist and a vet is a good idea. "I have always enjoyed and excelled in the sciences and see a career in veterinary medicine as an excellent way of combining my love of and respect for animals with my skills and abilities in science." This says "I want to work with animals" whilst avoiding sounding about four years old! Anyone who is tempted to write "I want to be a vet as I prefer to work with animals than humans" should place their application in the bin now because if that is anything close to what you write that is exactly where your application will be tossed when it hits the admissions tutors' desks. Being a good vet is as much about working with people as it is with animals – more so in fact. Even with non general practice based veterinary careers human contact and the need to communicate effectively with people forms an absolutely fundamental part of being successful. Vets working in laboratories with test animals still need to communicate daily with technicians, scientists and their managerial counterparts despite not having to deal with the classic 'owner.' Vets in industry, education, government, and practice all have to communicate with humans. There is not a single veterinary career path that we can think of that does not call upon your ability and willingness to talk to or otherwise communicate with other human beings. So, not only do we have to be master animal handlers but we also need to be great at conveying and eliciting information from our fellow man (and woman). So, a more useful statement may read something like "I believe veterinary science offers a career in which I am able to combine my desire to work with animals and apply my scientific skills and knowledge with my excellent ability to communicate effectively." This instantly tells the admissions tutor that you have thought hard about why you want to be a vet and not a doctor and that you appreciate, and indeed relish the fact, that we are very much in a 'people-centred' profession whether you'd realised it by this stage or not.

b) *Outline your work experience to date.*
This paragraph should be used to summarise not only what placements you have done but what you gained from them in terms of lessons learned and skills developed. Emphasise the diversity of your placements and describe any particularly interesting cases. There is a very good chance that this section will be discussed during your interview so write it well and please make sure that if you mention having done a placement that you a) have actually done it – remember, the interviewing panel can smell bullshit a mile off; and b) that you can recall the details readily and expand on them when asked in interview. It is also perfectly acceptable to take a casebook to your interview with you. The chances are that the interviewers will not look at it but having one sitting in front of you communicates a lot to the panel about your organisation, commitment and planning and so can work as a nice non-verbal selling-point. Another important, and hopefully obvious, point to make at this stage is that this section should only be used to summarise the work placements that you have already done and not refer to those placements that you intend to complete, unless you have definite dates booked. The vet schools are only interested in 'experience' and not 'potential experience.' If you are applying for deferred entry, however, then it is reasonable and in fact advisable to outline any planned placements in a later paragraph, as, again, this will likely be discussed at interview.

One area in which it is easy to casually slip up with regards to work experience is spending far too much time focusing on complex, very technical aspects of practice and overlooking the simpler yet vital parts of practice such as vaccination and preventative treatment. How many of you can claim to have spent weeks standing in on consults with a vet and yet find it almost impossible to describe what diseases we vaccinate dogs and cats against and when we do so? Chances are that you will be in this boat. We most certainly have been. So, please ensure that before you go for interview 'revise' some of the absolute basics of practice: what diseases we vaccinate against and when we do so; how often we worm animals and treat against fleas. The key point to make here is that approximately 80% of a vet's day-to-day work is derived from these 'bread and butter' matters so it is vital that you have a good understanding of why and how they are done. You'll feel a bit silly if you have claimed to have spent weeks and weeks 'in practice' and yet draw a blank expression when asked to name two of the diseases we routinely vaccinate puppies against.

c) *How do you relate to people?*
As discussed earlier, veterinary medicine is very much a 'people oriented' profession despite our main focus being on animals. Not only do the majority of us have clients to deal with but we also need to work closely with a team of colleagues, both within our own immediate working environment and in a wider capacity as we may call upon the advice and services of such people as specialists. For anyone who has done any work experience you will know that as a vet we get to work with a very broad range of people and will rely on our honed communication skills to do so effectively. Receptionists, nurses, senior vets, your fellow veterinary assistants – you need to be able to work well with all of them in order to function as a good vet. Often, the manner in which you interact with each of these groups will be slightly different. For example, chances are that as a vet student you will be able to relax and have a laugh with the nursing team whilst obviously showing them the respect that they deserve – this means listening to their advice and where possible helping them out by mucking in and not doing the 'them and us' thing that I have seen too many young vets unfortunately do where the nurses are considered and treated as second class citizens in the practice. This will contrast, however, to the way in which you will interact with the practice partners who, generally, will be older and with whom it may not be appropriate to joke about with the same way you do with the younger members of the team. There are always exceptions however and we know some practice partners and senior vets who you could happily treat like your best mate. The golden rule, as far as we are concerned, when thinking of how to relate and work with others is to put yourself in the other person's shoes

and imagine how you, yourself, would like to be treated. Everyone expects, rightly so, to be shown respect by their colleagues and as long as you bear this in mind then you'll be fine. Give examples on your statement of times that you contributed as an effective member of a team, for example, if you helped prep a patient for surgery or assisted the vet with a morning of TB testing by being the person in charge of keeping records up to date. Any such examples will demonstrate to the interviewers that you are able to work effectively with people and can adapt usefully to unfamiliar surroundings and circumstances – a vital veterinary skill.

d) *Give an indication of career direction, even if it is very tentative at this stage.*

Some of you will know even now that your future lies in equine surgery or that your destiny is to become the world's authority on gecko internal medicine. If you have a very clear and strong idea about your future career direction then say so as it will demonstrate further commitment to veterinary medicine and will provide an interesting talking point at interview. However, also make sure that you acknowledge the fact that even though you have no intention of ever touching a cow again post-graduation the course encompasses all aspects of veterinary and you are expected to gain experience, work with, study and pass examinations in all species. Even if you don't have any strong ideas about where you may end up in your career that is fine as many people change their ideas and career plans as they progress through the course. We know many of our colleagues, for example, who started vet school convinced that they were going to become equine surgeons to eventually go on and excel in small animal orthopaedics instead. Such is the variety and scope of the vet course that there are a hundred and one different potential career paths open to graduates and not having a firm, fixed plan at this stage is not going to be detrimental to your application in any way. If you are unsure exactly where your veterinary future may lie then say so, but in a proactive thoughtful manner, for example by saying that "although I don't have any firm ideas about where my career path lies I do believe that a career in veterinary medicine offers the opportunity to develop skills across many disciplines including research. I very much look forward to developing my skills and knowledge in all veterinary related fields." This simple statement communicates that you accept the vet course is a broad, general training platform and that it is not vital to select a specific career path at this stage.

Mentioning 'research' as an option is a good idea, even if you have absolutely no plans of ever going down the research route. There is a very real shortage of qualified veterinarians employed in veterinary, and indeed non-veterinary, scientific research and is an area that the universities are trying very hard to work on. This includes offering veterinary undergraduates the opportunity to 'intercalate' for a year whereby you would leave the vet course and join the final year of another, predominantly science, degree course earning an extra degree in that year and gaining excellent experience of original research through working on a final year project. Intercalation is well worth considering as at no other point in your life will you be offered the chance to earn a second degree in exchange for one more year at university, which in the grand scheme of things actually amounts to no time at all especially when you consider that the average vet course is five years in length. Financially it often makes sense too as not only will you be increasing your earning potential, often being able to ask for higher starting salaries than your non-intercalating peers, but an intercalated degree, especially if an upper second class or first is achieved, opens up potential career paths that may not have otherwise been open to you and which you may not have previously considered. There is also the fact that intercalation not only enables you to gain a second degree in a third of the normal time but also that this second degree will cost you no more than a year studying for your veterinary degree. In other words you will be charged the same level of tuition fees as an undergraduate studying for their first degree rather than having to pay post-graduate fees. As such the return on your time and monetary investment of intercalating is potentially very great. Couple this with the fact that universities are so keen for medics, dentists and vets to intercalate that very healthy bursaries and scholarships are often available to ease the financial strain of an additional year of studying and to act as an incentive to do so. In fact, some students almost end up making money on their extra year by attracting such levels of funding and being able to engage in part-time work during the extra vacations. It would be a smart move to mention in your application that intercalation is something that you would seriously consider, especially as you appreciate the need for veterinarians with an excellent level of research training. The crux of the matter is that universities are principally research driven institutes and the vast majority of the academic staff teaching you are employed by the university to conduct original research. For some academics, then, their primary focus is not on teaching you but on their research so if you can demonstrate an interest, even if it is fleeting and general, in research as a potential career path then you will interest the academic interview panellists.

f) *Any special achievements or responsibilities?*
Whether these are animal or non-veterinary in nature their aim is to demonstrate additional skills and attributes that you possess which make you a good candidate for a veterinary career. Do you have, or have you had, a part-time job? Yes? Well, mention it and describe what attributes you have as a result of it. For example, if you have worked as a customer services assistant in a shop then discuss how you developed empathetic skills and demonstrated responsibility in your role. Have you won any sporting awards, or other accolades? If so then, again, detail them in your statement as they will provide further evidence of certain key attributes that will potentially make you a great vet. Winning in sport requires dedication, commitment, organisation, sacrifice, focus, skill, teamwork (especially if your achievement was in a team sport) and a whole host of other positive traits. All of these will make you stand out in the eyes of the selectors and will also highlight the important fact that you have interests outside of academia and veterinary.

g) *Any additional interests or hobbies?*
As discussed, it is important to selectors that you are a well rounded and adjusted individual who will be able to cope with the tough academic rigours of the veterinary course and the pressures placed on you as both a vet student and ultimately as a vet. This is why it is important that you can demonstrate that you are able to switch off from the books occasionally and have something outside of studying to focus on and relax through. Obviously there will be plenty of opportunity to 'relax' at vet school but going out and getting plastered with your mates doesn't qualify as a hobby and its probably best not to mention it in your statement – let's just say that it will be quietly assumed that you like, or will certainly do so at university, going out with friends. Do you play a sport or a musical instrument? Do you write creatively or indulge in the arts? What about entrepreneurial endeavours or an interest in business affairs? Maybe you're a keen debater or fundraiser. Whatever it is you do outside of

school and that can be used to demonstrate positive character traits they should be mentioned in your personal statement. Again, the key rule here is to be honest and not over-egg the pudding by claiming to do more than you actually do. Again, this section will provide interesting material for discussion in an interview and it would be awkward at the least to have to wriggle out of something that you have written in your statement. Be honest, be sincere and this way you will be able to relax and talk openly and enthusiastically about those aspects of your life outside of studying that you enjoy.

Referees report:

Once you have completed, reviewed, spell-checked, reviewed and asked someone else to review your personal statement and initial parts of your application then you'll need to pass your application, along with the fee, to the person who is going to be writing your reference. The referee report is intended to support your application by highlighting certain achievements, mainly academic but also those of a sporting or community nature, and to offer additional information and recommendations that commend you to the selectors.

Supporting Documentation:

Some vet schools will ask for additional information to be provided in support of your application. Examples include some schools sending out 'work experience questionnaires' to candidates prior to interview. Expect the admissions department to follow up on any information you submit so, again, it's important to be honest in the information you give and do not be tempted to over-embellish your achievements and experience. It's always a good idea if you can to ask placement providers for a reference at the end of your time with them, but do not send these with your UCAS application as they will not be sent to the universities. Rather take them with you to interview where they may be looked at if the interviewers see them in front of you. Don't be disappointed if they don't get looked at though as there often isn't enough time to look at more than your personal statement during an interview. They can, if anything, act as a much needed confidence booster just before going in for your interview. If you have completed any research projects which you have mentioned as part of your application then it may be a good idea to have a copy of the report with you in case asked for it. Casebooks can also be a handy thing to have with you at interview although, again, don't be surprised if they don't get looked at. If anything simply having something neat, tidy and well organised sitting in front of you during the interview can be both comforting for you and also give the impression that you are serious, organised and mean business.

Mature candidates:

If there is insufficient space on your personal statement to cover your most important achievements then, initially, review your statement to see whether it can be condensed in order to fit more information in to the same space. Alternatively, you could prepare a separate CV and send this to the admissions tutors once you have submitted your application and have a UCAS reference number to quote.

Rejected?

If you do find yourself in the position of being rejected then contact the admissions tutors to ask for feedback. Some will gladly offer this whilst others may be too busy to be able to do so. Either way acknowledge and thank them for any correspondence. Often the main reason for candidates being rejected is that they have insufficient work experience. If this is the case then aim to rectify this before the A-level results are released as applications are reviewed in light of these and you may find that they are able to offer you a place if someone else doesn't achieve the grades given as part of a conditional offer. However, this will only apply if you have had an interview. If you are rejected as a result of not achieving the relevant grades then the advice is to contact the relevant admissions tutors as soon as possible for advice as fewer retake candidates are being considered these days. As such, it is important to get the university's opinion on your chances of successfully reapplying with retakes before you put yourself through the trials of doing so. If you do think that you may struggle to achieve the A's and B's that are the target grades you need to be aiming for at A-level then plan to overcome this obstacle as early as possible. It is generally easier to gain maximum marks at AS level than A2 so aim to maximise your achievements early on and aim to resit AS units if possible. Your options for resits are obviously dependent upon a number of factors including your school's policy on permitting retakes, the exam board you are with which will determine when retakes are possible, and the number of units you have already retaken. If there are extenuating circumstances for why you are likely to miss or have indeed missed your predictions then advise the universities as soon as possible as they will take this into consideration when reviewing your application. These may also be covered as part of the referee's report submitted with your application.

Example Personal Statement (Section 10)

Below is a copy of Matt's very own personal statement, followed by a commentary on some of the questions actually asked of him in his Bristol interview and how they relate directly to what has been written in his statement. We have highlighted the key phrases and sections of the statement.

My constant endeavour will be to ensure the welfare of animals committed to my care. A career as a Veterinary Surgeon would allow me to develop and apply my strong interest in science to the prevention, diagnosis and treatment of illness in animals. I find the husbandry and welfare aspects of caring for small and large animals highly rewarding. Being a veterinary surgeon encompasses all of the criteria I would look for in a career; teamwork, continual professional development and working closely with people. My desire to read veterinary medicine has been strengthened by the work experience I have gained, outlined below:

2 Years Barnfield House Veterinary Centre, including 5 full weeks and Saturday morning surgery (small animals)
2 weeks Elizabeth Smith Veterinary Surgery (mixed small animal and equine)
2 weeks Scotland Farm   2 weeks Mayhew Animal Home
(Dairy Farm)
1 week Bucks Meadow Riding   1 week Packington Fields Pig Farm
School
1 day Tynsdale Large Animal Practice

I have also attended both 'Vetsim' and 'Vetsix' courses and lectures on parasitology and navicular disease. These have given me an additional insight into the variety and breadth of work within the profession.

Working at Barnfield House Veterinary Centre has given me a comprehensive insight into small animal veterinary work. I have formed good working relationships with all the members of the team as well as with the animals and their owners. It has given me the opportunity to follow interesting cases from the initial diagnosis, throughout treatment to final recovery. I have developed a special interest in emergency small animal surgery. At Scotland Farm I took a 'hands on' role working with the herd of 180 dairy cows. The tasks I completed included milking twice daily, as well as stripping the foremilk to check for mastitis. I was also given the task of vaccinating cows against Leptospirosis, fitting ear tags and castrating bulls. My work experience has highlighted the differences between caring for an individual animal in comparison to that of a herd as well as balancing the commercial and welfare aspects of farming.

In 2003 I was a finalist for the Edexcel Young Achiever of the Year Award. I have gained my Gold Duke of Edinburgh Award and Queen Scout Award. I completed the expedition elements of both of these awards by canoeing and I now wish to continue by becoming an instructor. Last year I represented the UK at the World Scout Jamboree in Thailand. Recently I was selected to participate in a Public Speaking and Relations course to promote scouting. I have taken a team leader role in assisting at my local Beaver Scout colony for the past three years. At Hatch End High I was appointed as Head Boy. Through this role I developed my leadership, organisation and communication skills, which will be invaluable in my career as a Veterinary Surgeon.

Matt was called for interview at Bristol in 2004. As you will be able to see from the questions he was asked a lot of the interview is guided directly by what you have said in your personal statement. This highlights the real importance of, first, writing a great statement and, secondly, knowing your statement inside and out before arriving. You should really be able to recite your statement from memory and be ready to expand on any part of it if asked.

Bristol Interview (1st December 2004) – Questions asked:

1. **How was your journey? Did you find the vet school ok?**
   A standard question to break the ice and ease you into the interview. The important thing to remember is that the interviewers are not out to trip you up and make you suffer but want you to feel relaxed so they can then see the real you.

2. **What do you vaccinate a dog against?**
    Having said in the personal statement that you have undertaken a significant amount of work experience in a small animal practice this is a fairly obvious question choice, and one that you should be expected to be able to answer. Any given day at a small animal surgery will have numerous appointments for boosters and being able to answer this question shows that you have been paying attention whilst seeing practice.

3. **Tell me about leptospirosis.**
    If you have stated that you have spent time vaccinating a herd of cows against a specific disease you should be expected to be able to give at least a brief overview of the main points of it, including the symptoms you may see and any treatments we may use.

4. **How would you treat this disease?**
    A good follow up question, testing basic understanding that bacterial disease is treated with antibiotics. Whilst the interviewer will not expect you to name the specific antibiotic you would use they will be searching for you to employ sound logic in regards to where the antibiotic acts in the body and what the best method would be to give it. This is a perfect example of having to combine knowledge from work experience and school in order to reach a novel answer to a question the answer to which you would not have known before walking into the interview. This is the sort of cool on-the-spot thinking that admissions tutors look for. Being able to answer questions under pressure and generally handle stress is an important veterinary skill.

5. **What do you know about MRSA?**
    This question, again, follows on nicely from the preceding question on antibiotics and aims to test the interviewee on their knowledge of current affairs and to see if you really do have a 'strong interest in science'. Again, whilst a textbook answer of MRSA is not expected, you should have a basic understanding, including knowing something of other important multi-resistant bacteria. A lot of the important work that vets are involved in concerns zoonoses, or diseases of animals that can infect humans.

As a result there is quite a lot of crossover between veterinary science and human medicine and interviewers will be checking your understanding of this.

6. **BSE was a major problem in the UK. What can you tell me about this disease?**
Answering this question relies on the interviewee having spent some time either talking to a vet or looking into at literature about this particular disease. The understanding that the causative agent is a prion and not a bacterium or virus is crucial.

7. **What can you tell me about proteins?**
Again, a good follow-on as the interview shifts back and forth from testing veterinary knowledge to school knowledge by asking the candidate to link knowledge of proteins with the disease process involved in BSE. Questions like this should give any interviewee the opportunity to shine.

8. **You say you have a special interest in small animal emergency surgery. Can you describe to me what you would do if you were presented with a GDV?**
Including such a bold and sweeping statement in your personal statement could easily result in a question like this and you should expect to be asked a question relating to any specific career plans you have talked about. The interviewers are now testing whether you were actually telling the truth in your personal statement, or whether you included something just because you thought it would sound more impressive. If the latter is true then it is these sorts of question that will show you up. However, if you really do have a special interest in small animal emergency surgery then talking for a couple of minutes about a fairly common problem afflicting deep-chested dogs should be an excellent opportunity to show   off.

9. **What can you tell me about treatment options for Navicular Disease?**
If you have accompanied vets to a CPD (continuing professional development) talk this is a fantastic thing to put down on your

personal statement. However, you should be able to then discuss the main points of the talk and demonstrate that you've tried to understand what was being taught. In this case a basic knowledge of the treatment options and their pros and cons shows the interviewer that you were able to digest and take in some of the main points from the talk. This will strongly suggest that you will be able to cope with the style of teaching used at veterinary school.

10. **Thank you very much. Do you have any questions you'd like to ask us before you leave?**
By no means should you feel like you have to ask a question. However, it can be another opportunity to show not only your commitment to the course but also the university you are applying to. In his Bristol interview Matt used this time to discuss intercalated BSc degrees – something that most vet schools will offer and be keen for candidates to consider. Whilst at the time he had no intention of undertaking one half-way through his degree, a friend, who was studying at the time, said they were very keen on promoting them. As a result, a well thought-out question on the subject impressed the interviewers.

Matt must have impressed the interviewers with his statement and answers as he received an offer from Bristol, as well as London and Glasgow.

Entry Requirements

The basic entry requirements for most of the vet schools are essentially similar in terms of the academic and work experience criteria. It will be expected that candidates will have a good set of grades at high school level, especially in the core subjects of English, science and maths, and similarly high grades at AS level or their equivalent, as well as excellent predictions. Candidates should realistically be aiming to achieve B grades or higher at both these stages, with both science at GCSE and, in most cases, chemistry at A-level being at grade A. The reasons for this have already been discussed and it is fair to say that if you haven't achieved this minimum then your chances of being accepted onto a vet course are slim as a healthy proportion of the applicants will have these grades. A summary of the main academic requirements is provided in an earlier chapter but it is a good idea to check with the individual universities regarding their specific application requirements and this can be done in a number of ways:

1. University and individual course prospectuses – read, digest and internalise these as they will provide much of the basic information you will be looking for. Most of these will now be available online but if you are unable to access them electronically then contact the course admissions tutors who will happily send out printed copies to you. It is vitally important that you do read these prospectuses as asking a question at interview for which the answer can be found easily in the prospectus will cast you in a fairly poor light as someone who has neglected to do even basic research on the course and university. The interviewers' opinion will be "well, if you can't be bothered with us then why should we be bothered with you?" So get hold of them early and make them your new favourite bedtime reading.

2. University websites – pretty much the same aim as above. See the appendix at the end of the book for website addresses.

3. University admissions staff – there is nothing wrong with contacting the admissions department to ask for clarification on points either not covered in the prospectuses or which are unclear. The main point here is that you have already looked at the available information as, again, it does not reflect well if you ring to ask questions when the answers are already available. If in doubt, however, then give them a call as they will be happy to help.

Most schools will make offers to A-level students of something like 'AAB' or more rarely 'ABB.' Chemistry will often be expected at grade A with the choice over preferred additional subjects varying between schools, although there is still a preference for at least one other science to be studied, whether it be maths, physics or biology, although the latter is preferred. Some of the schools are making efforts to widen access and the appeal of veterinary as a career option by considering applicants with non-traditional A-level subjects, such as a humanities subject (eg geography) or the arts. Subjects that, to our knowledge, are still not considered are general studies, drama, PE and critical thinking. This list is subject to change and if in doubt it is always advisable to consult the individual course prospectus or admissions department.

Richard Dixon BVMS PhD CertVR MRCVS

Richard Dixon is Founder and Group Managing Director of Vets Now. Having qualified as a vet in 1993 from Glasgow University, Richard worked in general practice before returning to Glasgow where he gained his RCVS certificate in Veterinary Radiology followed in 2000 by a PhD in Canine Thyroid Disease. In 2001 Richard established Vets Now Ltd., the country's largest dedicated provider of emergency and out-of-hours veterinary care. The company has gone from strength to strength winning numerous accolades and Richard himself has been the recipient of several prestigious awards including the Entrepreneurial Exchange's Emerging Entrepreneur of the Year 2005.

1. **Did you always know you'd run your own company?**
   No, not at all. I'd wanted to be a vet from a very early age and always assumed that I would go into mixed practice and spend my career doing the traditional aspects of the job. When I was doing my PhD at Glasgow I did a lot of emergency work and noticed that there were certain changes occurring in that vets wanted more of a work-life balance, wanting to offer a great out-of-hours service but have a life as well. A lot of vets realised that it wasn't really possible to be able to achieve both. I also noticed how as the veterinary profession became more high profile expectations and demands on vets by clients became greater. Clients were no longer simply satisfied with being able to get hold of a tired vet at 4am but wanted a consistently high standard of care whenever needed. As such an opportunity existed to service both the veterinary profession and pet-owners.

2. **Were you very entrepreneurial at school or university?**
Not at school, no, but at university I was always involved in lots of extracurricular activities such as The Chronicle and sports teams. After graduating I did a certificate in entrepreneurship at Strathclyde University, which I really enjoyed and which opened my mind to business.

3. **Some people argue that it is impossible to be both a great clinician and businessman – do you agree with this?**
In a word, no. Anyone who subscribes to this line of thinking is living in a fantasy world. Vets need to be more accepting of the fact that veterinary medicine is a business and that profit is not a dirty word but essential if we want to then invest in the business and improve standards of clinical care. A lot of people miss out on business and are not aware of the commercial aspects of the veterinary profession. I think this is due to the fact that a lot of graduates view veterinary medicine simply as a vocational career whereas a lot of practice actually requires vets to really get involved with running the business. By developing the business side of the veterinary profession we can invest in improving clinical care and boost morale.

4. **Do you advocate some teaching of business in vet schools then?**
I would advocate some business teaching in the undergraduate course but I believe the main aim is for graduates to have some awareness of the business aspects of being a vet and for it not to be a dirty word. It would be good to have some business teaching but I realise it's difficult to fit it into an already packed schedule.

5. **What do you do to relax in your spare time?**
Golf! It's the most relaxing sport ever and I try to play whenever I have a chance. I'm currently playing off a handicap of 13.5 but my aim is 7 by the age of 40.

6. **Do you have any pets?**
Yes, loads. We have a couple of dogs, a cat, sheep, ducks and, until recently, some turkeys although Mr Fox managed to get to them. I also have a Giant African Land Snail – I'm not sure why though as they seem the most pointless pet!

7. **What would you have done if you weren't a vet?**

Hmm, well i've always wanted to be a vet but if I was to do anything else then I'd have liked to have been an astronaut. The thought of going into space sounds amazing.

8. **What top tips would you offer any vet students with business aspirations?**

Be open-minded and seek as much input and advice from others as you can. Vets are generally very driven, focused and used to being in control so it's important when running a business to be able to make that mental shift from controlling everything and to be open to influence and surround yourself with people who have passion and expertise in other areas. You can't do everything yourself and so it's important to have great people around you and realise that this is not a weakness but rather a strength. I have been lucky enough to have a great team of people around me and we believe it's important to allow our vets and other team members to make their mark on the business and to help create something better for the future.

9. **What are the best and worst parts of your job?**

The best part is all the learning I have had to do and continue to do, and thus being professionally challenged all of the time. The worst part is getting complaints. I hate any complaint and they make me feel physically sick, even if I know we haven't done anything wrong. Thankfully though we don't get many.

10. **What do you see as the main challenges for the profession over the next five years?**

I think the profession is facing more bureaucracy and certainly more competition. Vets need to make that mental step and accept that competition is a fact of life and not demeaning. Historically clients have just listened to and accepted what their vet has told them. This, however, is changing as clients become more educated and demanding. We need to realise that clients and consumers are guiding the profession and our role is to guide and educate rather than dictate to pet owners. It's also important to realise that more competition means that if we don't listen to clients then they will simply vote with their feet and go elsewhere. Our challenge then, as vets, is to balance catering to the expectations of clients whilst maintaining animal welfare.

11. **What does the future hold for you?**

Vets Now is constantly evolving. We have just appointed a new MD so I can spend more time focusing on future opportunities and continuing to learn.

12. **What top three tips would you give prospective vet students?**

First of all, be passionate about veterinary as it is a tough job with pay that isn't great. Personally I was told when I was an undergraduate that being a vet was tough and not paid very well but I went ahead and did it anyway which I think is typical for most aspiring vets! Secondly, you need to have a heightened awareness of the fact that as a vet you deal with owners, not just animals. Handling owner expectations and being aware of the fact that you're entering a people based business are very important. Being good at either clinical skills or dealing with people doesn't necessarily make you a good vet – you need to have balance. Thirdly, I urge new graduates to maintain social contact with other people, vets or otherwise. This could be through getting involved in local sports teams or other activities. Staying in contact with university friends and establishing new contacts and support networks is vital especially as you go from vet school where you are used to knowing everyone and having people around you all the time to an often quite isolated job. This can be a difficult transition and we are all too aware of how high the suicide rate is for vets. So, maintain social contacts!

Improving the lives of vets & pets

For further information on Vets Now see the website *www.vets-now.com*

Interviews

According to figures from the vet schools approximately one third of applicants are offered interviews so the chances of getting to this vital stage are probably a lot better than most of you had probably feared. If you do make it to interview then the first thing to do is congratulate yourself as you've already done extremely well and it is obvious that something about you caught the admissions tutor's eye, which is always a good thing. Most of the schools hold their interviews between November and March although the Cambridge colleges usually interview earlier, with the majority of these being conducted in December. This likely reflects the slightly more complicated process for applying to Oxbridge, including, quite often, the need to sit specific supplementary papers or have multiple interviews. Either way the interview is probably the single most important stage as this is when candidates either sink or swim and thus attract or miss out on those much coveted offers.

Why bother interviewing? Well, the reasons universities interview candidates rather than just allocating places based on your UCAS applications are many-fold. First, it's a great way of checking whether you actually wrote your application yourself or got your parents to complete it as the interviews are face-to-face, with just you and a panel of interviewers so everything you do or say is directly from you. It may seem cynical to suggest this as a reason but it's accepted that it's getting harder and harder to gain a place and with increased competition comes increased temptation for some candidates to try and 'gain the upper hand' by asking someone else, who may have a better grasp of language perhaps, to fill in their form. Secondly, the vet schools want to meet you in order to get to know you a little better. They want to make sure that you are really as enthusiastic and focused as you say you are and that you seem like a candidate who will realistically be able to cope with the trials and rigours of the vet course. It's almost impossible to meaningfully glean any of this sort of information from a single A4 statement, most of which will read fairly similarly anyway. It's only by meeting a person face to face that you can really attempt to form any meaningful judgements about them, with everything from your body language to the way you answer challenging questions and even casual, friendly questions being analysed during an interview. The interviewers know how precious vet school places are and so want to be absolutely sure that they offer them only to those candidates who will really benefit from the course and who will potentially be of benefit to the profession. Ask yourself, if you were running a prestigious company and you were hiring for an important job would you seriously give someone the job without even meeting them? Unlikely. In an ideal world most interviewers would like to be able to spend a week with you, observing you as you go about your daily life but due to the time constraints of interviewing and the fact that we don't live in a Big Brother type state this is not possible. As such, most vet schools will have no more than twenty minutes in which to 'get to know you' and make the decision over whether you deserve an offer or not.

So what does it take to interview well? Entire books have been written on this subject and although there is no such thing as the perfect method, there are a few basic rules to follow. The main thing to communicate at a veterinary interview is your enthusiasm. This is achieved through your body language and also the things you say as well as the way you say them. For example, do you slouch in to the interview with your head down or walk in with your head held high and a friendly, enthusiastic smile on your face? Which person would you rather talk to? The other key rule, and more important in fact than confidence, which will come naturally if you do this correctly, is preparation. "To fail to prepare is to prepare to fail." Basic preparation such as reading over your application and knowing the answers to a few very simple veterinary questions, such as what we vaccinate dogs and cats against, is an essential step as it will give you the confidence necessary to go in and be able to be yourself and to formulate answers to questions posed. The more preparation you do then generally the more relaxed you should be able to feel going into the interview and we all know that it's much easier to think clearly when we're relaxed than when we're c*@ping ourselves! As well as swotting up on basic knowledge, working on good interview technique is also an important preparation with the best way to do it being practice. Mock interviews are a great idea as they enable you to make all of your basic, elementary, silly mistakes when it's not important so that when it comes to the real thing you will be a lean, mean interview machine. Mock interviews are great for getting a feel for the type of pressure that you may be placed under on the day or to analyse your body language and correct it if need be. You'll be amazed at what subtle things we can communicate with our bodies without being even aware. If you can, try to video your mock interviews so you can watch them back and identify things you did well and potential areas for improvement. It will feel weird to watch yourself but the exercise can really pay dividends if it helps you to become better at being interviewed. Besides, most of the vet schools now run communication skills sessions as part of their curriculum, part of which often involves getting vet students to video themselves during mock consultation scenarios. Again, they usually find it a strange and alien experience to start with but very soon come to value it as an extremely useful weapon in the self-improvement arsenal. Who should you ask to give a mock interview? Anyone and everyone really. The best people to ask are perhaps one of your teachers or a vet at the practice you go to. It's probably better to avoid asking parents or friends however as the chances are you'll be too relaxed with them and it won't provide an authentic interview experience. Try to make the mock interview as similar to the real one as possible by arranging to conduct it over approximately twenty to thirty minutes, preferably in an unfamiliar, official feeling room and dress as if you were attending the real interview. The aim is to essentially desensitise yourself to the interview process so that rather than be paralysed with fear on the day of the real thing you will be able to concentrate on what really matters which is thinking clearly and making the best impression on the interviewers as you can. One of the benefits of analysing a mock interview is that you will able to see what it is that the interviewers will be able to see on actual interview day. As such you will quickly come to realise how important your visual presentation and the all important first impressions really are. How many of you have looked at a new kid at school wearing glasses and instantly thought, "geek?" Most of you is our guess. What you would have been doing is making an immediate judgement based on first impressions – those little bits of information we communicate silently and which other people pick up on and rightly or wrongly form their initial judgements about you based upon. The interviewers will be no different. They're people too. So expect them to look at you as you walk in to your interview and form instant, first impression-based, judgements about you. Obviously during the course of the interview as you talk and communicate more fully with the panel their initial impressions and judgements may be altered in light of the new information which you are communicating to them. However, it's far easier to build upon a good first impression than it is to try and claw your way back from a bad one. How you dress and walk in to the interview room is therefore as important as how much you know about what current issues are important. Walk in confidently, with your chin up, shoulders back and a warm smile. If the interviewers go to shake your hand then reciprocate and shake each person's hand firmly, trying to match but not exceed the pressure exerted by the person initiating the handshake. To attempt to be the dominant shaker may suggest to the interviewer that you are an overbearing and intimidating individual; too weak and limp and you scream out that you're weak and can be trodden all over. Either impression is a bad one. If no one goes to shake your hand then don't be offended – you may simply be the one hundredth candidate they have seen that day and they are simply tired and past the hand-shaking phase. Wait to be invited to sit and if no-one offers a seat then enquire as to where you should take a seat. Again, this is simple, good interview etiquette. Just bundling in and grabbing the first empty seat that you see may communicate that you're either grabby and just take what you want or that you're so tired from having run all the way to the interview from your house that you can't possibly wait to be invited to sit! Remember, the interview room is the interviewers' territory and as such they will expect to be the ones calling the shots. Things like walking in and just sitting down before being invited or before the interviewers sit down just screams a lack of respect. Sit up straight but avoid looking like you have a burning poker up your *&£$ and try to lean forward slightly – this makes you appear keen and engaged. Do not slouch back in either a 'too cool for school' or over-cocky, over comfortable manner and don't, unless you're a girl and are wearing a skirt, cross your legs. The best position to adopt in any interview is a fairly neutral body position, with weight distributed evenly through your body and a slight lean forward. Be mindful as well of what you are doing with your hands. Lots of us, when nervous, will engage our hands in activity by, for example, playing with our hair or drumming our fingers on the desk. Don't! Not only could this be deemed as incredibly annoying by the interviewers, who you are trying to impress not irritate after all, but it will also scream out how nervous you are. If you do need to use your hands then use them to illustrate and gesture during your answers – try to watch some footage on the web of some famous speeches and watch how the speakers use their hands. Try to emulate them but don't do anything that doesn't feel natural for you. Another important aspect of body language to keep in mind is your use of eye contact. Maintain fairly good levels of eye contact with your interviewers but do not stare. A good idea is to draw an imaginary line from one eye to the other and then to their mouth, forming a triangle and to then allow your eyes to follow the lines, periodically breaking away to look down at your notes, for example. If there is more than one interviewer, which is common, then frequently look to each member to engage all of them. Good eye contact communicates trustworthiness and honesty as well as confidence in what you are saying. Avoiding eye contact, on the other hand, or routinely breaking any contact that is established is often translated as a sign of dishonesty and may make you appear to be undeserving of trust. Speak clearly and deliberately and try not to rush. This is where recording yourself doing a mock interview will help as most of us will unconsciously speed up our speech when we are nervous.

In terms of basic information to cover and be familiar with prior to any interview the starting point has to be your own personal statement from your UCAS application as this will form the basis of most of what is discussed in the interview. Read, reread and completely internalise your statement and ensure that you are in a position to readily elaborate on any points in it. The next step is to know the basics about the vet schools you are applying to and especially the one that is currently interviewing you. Thirdly, be in possession of the very basic bits of veterinary knowledge already aluded to in previous chapters. Fourth, make sure you are up to date and familiar with the main current issues affecting the veterinary profession, such as foot and mouth and bird flu, so that you are able to discuss them with the interviewers if asked.

One important thing to discuss is that the interviewers are looking more at *how* you answer questions, especially the tougher, more unorthodox ones, rather than what you actually say and whether it's right or wrong. They will be looking for a calm, rational and well thought-out response. So, if you are posed with a question the answer to which you are not immediately sure of then ask whether you could have a moment to think about it. The interviewers will be impressed to see that rather than rushing in with an answer – any answer – you are confident and prepared to take the initiative and care to consider your responses. This is an important skill to have when you're working as a vet as owners rely upon you to think carefully about diagnoses and treatment plans. If after careful consideration you still don't know the answer then admit it but don't just leave it at that. Rather, say that you don't know the answer now but when you leave the interview you will go and find out. This shows that you have the maturity and honesty to admit when you're not certain of something rather than just guess and that you are resourceful and keen enough to want to find out the correct answer.

Here are a few examples of potential interview questions that you may be asked as part of your interview:

1. **How was your journey here today?**
    This is a friendly starting question, intended to ease you into the interview and make you feel more relaxed. Take the opportunity to engage in some short, friendly sociable conversation before the interview is directed in more formal territory.

2. **Have you been to the University before?**
    Did you attend the open day? If so then elaborate on this. It is also a great opportunity to mention if you have visited the vet school in a non-official capacity previously, for example because you have a friend studying there. This will be of interest to the interviewers and will demonstrate your determination, resolve and resourcefulness in finding out as much about the vet school and university as you can. If, however, your only 'visit' to the vet school involved climbing over the wall and evading security then best not to mention it!

3. **What do you think of our prospectus?**
    You will have read it. If not then this constitutes a bit of an own goal! Have an opinion on it – what did you like? What did it tell you was unique about this particular vet school? This could lead on to topics of conversation such as your work experience.

4. **How do you think you're doing with your A-levels?**
    This is a great time to really sell yourself – if you are doing well then say so and highlight that you're working hard. If possible then try and steer the conversation onto a subject that you are particularly keen on and that has some veterinary focus.

5. **Why do you want to be a vet?**

    Potentially one of the most difficult questions you could be asked in interview and justifiably one that many applicants dread. How are you supposed to summarise a burning desire to read Veterinary Science that will convince your interviewers to give you a place?! It is a question that you will have no doubt been asked by many people since you first showed an interest in the profession and the simple answer is there is no simple answer! It may be best to avoid the simple clichés that are frequently banded about. A simple love of animals is unlikely to give you the motivation to stick out the course. Likewise, finding science 'fascinating' does not instantly make you a suitable candidate. Remember that the people interviewing you are likely to have heard the same answers from dozens of other hopeful applicants. Make what you say engaging and ensure you are enthusiastic. So, what are your motivations? More than likely there would have been an initial motivation. This could have been as widely varied as a parent who is a vet or a farmer to being inspired by a James Herriot novel. However, it is what you did after this initial inspiration that really would have made you want to pursue a career as a veterinary surgeon.

    Talking about work experience is an excellent way to demonstrate this. The time you have spent with both vets and animals shows a dedication to the profession. By having undertaken extensive work experience you will demonstrate to an interviewer that you appreciate all aspects of the job, both the highs and the lows, and are therefore making a well informed decision when you apply. It costs a vast amount of money to train every vet in the UK, and a major part of the admissions process is ensuring that only those who will stick out the five years of university and progress into practice or research are selected. You are after all an expensive investment. Another merit of mentioning your work experience and how it has motivated you is that it may easily lead onto further questioning about what you have seen. This will be a far more straightforward line of questioning (providing you were paying attention)!

There are many other reasons why you may want to be a vet. A veterinary degree is potentially the best science degree you can gain, especially in terms of breadth. In what other degree could you learn about anatomy, physiology, biochemistry, pathology, parasitology...the list is endless. The degree could open up a plethora of doors, including into industry and research. At present there are a lack of veterinary researchers, and thus whilst it may be unlikely that you are entirely motivated to enter the world of academia and research at this point, at least being aware of the options and expressing this interest is certainly a good reason to wish to study the course.

One final point to remember and reinforce is that you are fully aware that the job is hard work. Getting through university itself can be a struggle. However, through your work experience you not only appreciate this, but are prepared for the challenge. Whilst you will undoubtedly be nervous try to let your enthusiasm for the course shine through as it is this which will really help communicate your motivation and desire to be a vet.

6. **Why do you want to study at this university?**
    You may have convinced an admissions panel of your motivation to become a vet, but an equally important factor is why you want to take a place at their university. Obviously you are limited to four places you can apply to on your UCAS form, so how do you convince all of them -assuming you are called to interviews at each- that you want to go there? As a young, motivated individual it is essential that you are well read on the city you are applying to. Is there a particular aspect of the course that you like the look of? For instance, do you think that the integrated teaching style of Nottingham would suit you? Equally, would living in a city for all five years of the course, such as at Glasgow, be appealing to you? Picking up particular 'bonuses' of the university that is interviewing you shows not only a motivation to study there, but also strokes the ego of the interviewers! It is important that you are fully aware of how the university works, and have read the literature available. Being poorly informed about a place at which

you are being interviewed is poor form, and will do you no favours.

It is important to look not only into the course structure but the city itself. Can you see yourself living there for the next five years? Is there a particular facility locally that studying at the university will allow you to use? Living in Bristol or London will obviously be a good choice if you enjoy live music, for example, as large acts tend to tour through these cities. Your university experience is more than the sum of your studies alone, and thus other interests are important, not only in making you a well rounded person, but also in giving you a much needed release from the pressures of training to become a vet. Admissions tutors are more than aware of this, and if you can talk about a particular club or society that joining the university will allow you to join, they will see this as an extra incentive in offering you a place. As an example, one of the authors of this book stayed with a couple of final years he had met on a farm before one of his interviews. They took him out on a social that was occurring that night, with the consequence that he irresponsibly turned up to his interview the following day a little worse for wear. This must have been apparent, as a member of the interview panel questioned him on his previous night's activities. Upon telling them about it, they found the story highly amusing, sent someone to fetch him a cup of strong tea and a biscuit, before telling him that he would fit in well with the social life of the university's vets! Whilst we strongly discourage this kind of behaviour, it does demonstrate how the interview panels are looking for a certain type of person, and if you can show that you will fit in with the culture of that particular university, you are greatly strengthening your chances of receiving an offer.

7. **Tell us something about your work experience with animals.**
This is another of the big, important questions of the interview and it is important to avoid just reciting a list of the work experience placements that you have completed – the interviewers will have your statement and so will be aware of what you have done. What they are keen for you to elaborate on

are the lessons you learnt and whether you had any interesting experiences.

8. **What are the main lessons you have learned from your work experience?**
    This is a typical follow-up question and it is vital to indicate the variety of the placements you have seen. Emphasise the fact that you have learned that veterinary is very much a people-oriented industry and that the clinical side of veterinary is only one aspect of the whole, with business skills and awareness being as important for vets as clinical capability and knowledge. Try to illustrate your answers with personal examples. For example, "when I worked with a large animal vet TB testing I...."

9. **What do you vaccinate a dog/cat against?**
    A gift of a question for anyone who has seen small animal practice (which will be 99% of people applying to vet school)! As the majority of vets' consults will involve routine vaccinations, this is something that many of you will have seen innumerable times. However, have you picked up what is in those small vials?! For those of you who haven't, here it is again.

Dogs:- 1st vaccination at 8 weeks & 2nd vaccination at 10 weeks

*   *Distemper*

*   *Hepatitis*

*   *Parvovirus*

*   *Parainfluenza*

*   *Leptospirosis*

Whilst these are the main vaccines given, an increasing number of owners are electing to vaccinate against kennel cough. This is a general term given to an upper respiratory tract infection (essentially a very nasty cough) so called because of high prevalence when animals are housed close together, such as in a boarding kennel. For this reason, kennels will require that a dog is protected against this prior to allowing them to board. What makes this particular vaccine interesting is that the liquid is not injected under the skin, but instead squirted directly into the nose. The important thing to communicate to clients about kennel cough is that it is a syndrome caused by a variety of different respiratory infectious agents, from viruses to bacteria, and that the vaccine provides immunity against the main five or so. As a result, the vaccine is not 100% protective but certainly reduces the risk of developing kennel cough.

Dogs travelling under the PETS scheme are also required to have a vaccine against rabies. Blood tests are required prior to actually travelling to ensure that the animal has adequate protection.

Cats: - 1st vaccination at 9 weeks & 2nd vaccination at 12 weeks

- *Feline Calicivirus*

- *Feline Rhinotracheitis ('Cat Flu')*

- *Feline Infectious Enteritis (aka Panleukopaenia)*

- *FeLV (Feline Leukaemia Virus)*

When vaccinating cats it is important to ascertain what sort of lifestyle they lead. For example, if the cat does not leave the house, then it may not be necessary to vaccinate against FeLV.

With all of the vaccines it is important to carefully follow the instructions given by the drugs company. For example, the first course of injections should not be administered until the protection provided by the antibodies received from the mother has decreased, otherwise the vaccine may be less effective. It is important for a booster to be given a few weeks later, followed by yearly vaccinations in most cases.

Another factor to be aware of is the phenomenon of injection site carcinomas. In recent years it has become apparent that there may be a correlation between injecting an animal with FeLV vaccine and the development of a certain type of cancer. Whilst the chances of this are very small, and certainly not enough to justify electing not to vaccinate an animal, it is important to consider where the vet actually injects the animal. To this end, it is recommended that the FeLV vaccine be injected under the skin of one of the legs, typically the right hindleg. This is because it is easier to amputate a limb, should the cancer develop, than it is to remove an aggressive tumour from the scruff.

10. What do you know about spaying and castration?

These two surgical procedures are the bread and butter of any small animal surgeon's daily operations list. In fact, as a veterinary student you can expect the first surgical procedure you are likely to perform (under the constant and direct supervision of a qualified vet) to be a cat castrate. If you have seen any small animal work experience you will have almost certainly seen at least one of these procedures.

Every vet you watch will almost certainly have a different surgical approach to these operations, ranging from preferences for specific suture materials to whether prophylactic antibiotics are used. There are however several major differences between the species. Bitches are placed in dorsal recumbency (laying on their back) with a midline incision providing surgical access to the uterus. In comparison, queens (female cats) are spayed whilst in right lateral recumbency (laying on their right side), with the incision being made on their left flank, just in front of their left back leg. Performing an ovario-hysterectomy, which means removal of both the uterus and ovaries, in cats in such a manner is idiosyncratic to Britain. If you ever see practice with a vet from anywhere else in the world they are likely to approach spaying a cat in exactly the same way as a bitch.

One important point to remember is to always check the cat you are about to spay for testicles! An all too common mistake is for a vet to dive straight into surgery, spending an impossible amount of time looking for a uterus which does not exist, due to the clinical record stating incorrectly that they are female. They will almost certainly not make the same mistake again though, especially as explaining to an owner that their female cat is in fact male and has undergone abdominal surgery for no reason is not a pleasant experience!

In both the bitch and the queen it is essential to make sure all of the ovarian tissue is removed. Even a small remnant may remain functional and produce oestrogen and progesterone, the reproductive hormones. Therefore whilst the animal may no longer be able to become pregnant, they will still show the behaviours associated with their respective reproductive cycles. Of equal importance, the health benefits of performing the operation will be nullified.

With respects to castration, the surgical incisions are made on the scrotum in cats. A single prescrotal incision is used in the dog. As cat castrates are such a quick procedure you will often see vets induce and maintain the cat's anaesthesia with an injectable agent.

The main objective is always the same: in castrations, the removal of the testes and in spays, the complete removal of the uterus and ovaries. These procedures are irreversible and have the obvious consequence of rendering the animal unable to reproduce. This is often the main reason why an owner will elect to have these procedures performed.

Behaviours associated with the sex hormones will also be reduced, although if an older animal is being neutered then some of these behaviours may have been 'learnt'. In this case the removal of the gonads will have a limited effect in reducing the behaviours. It is important to make this point clear to owners, especially if their reasoning for castrating a dog is to reduce aggression.

One of the other major reasons for encouraging owners to have their pets neutered is to reduce their risk of developing specific types of cancer later in life, prinicipally testicular and prostatic tumours in the male, and mammary, or breast, ovarian, cervical and uterine tumours in the female. Spaying bitches before they are a year old, and prior to their first season, can reduce their lifetime risk of mammary tumours to less than 0.5% compared to a risk of 25% in entire bitches. If spayed after the second season or later there is little protective benefit against these tumours. Another health benefit is the prevention of a condition known as pyometra, which is an infection of the uterus in which it becomes filled with pus. This is a serious condition which makes the bitch very sick and requires emergency surgery to remove the enlarged and infected uterus, as well as aggressive antibiotic treatment.

On the flip side neutered cats and dogs are more prone to putting on weight if fed the same amount after surgery. This is easily avoided by simply reducing the amount of food fed after surgery, with the advice being to do so by about a third. Some people suggest that spaying before the first season increases the risk of developing urinary incontinence.

All animals that are rescued and re-homed will be neutered without exception to help in the constant fight against the thousands of unwanted and stray animals in the UK.

11. Have you ever felt scared of any animals?

No vet wants to admit that they are ever frightened of animals but the truth is that most will at some point during their career feel vulnerable and apprehensive when confronted with a patient. The key is to acknowledge the importance of having a healthy respect for the power and unpredictability of a lot of animals. Chris, for example, hasn't, to date, been bitten by a cat and plans to keep it that way. It's not because he's frightened of cats – although some are just plain terrifying – but rather that he doesn't underestimate them or their ability and willingness to use their teeth at any time! If you have found yourself in a potentially hair-raising situation with an animal then tell the interviewers about it, especially if it is quite funny.

12. What are your views on the use of animals in scientific research and teaching?

Whilst the view of the general public on animal testing may vary wildly it should always be remembered that as a veterinary surgeon it is something that you have to accept happens and understand the reasons for it. At present no new drug in this country may be licensed for either humans or animals unless it has first undergone stringent testing on animals. It is an inescapable fact that much of our current knowledge of basic science and medicine has come from animal testing. It is also important to note that all research involving the use of laboratory animals is closely monitored and scrutinised by the Home Office.

Experiments must receive approval before they can be carried out. The animals used are looked after by highly trained individuals and not exposed to any undue suffering. It is fair to say that the conditions that these animals are kept in will be far superior to many pets kept in the home.

This is not to say that the use of animals in scientific testing is always warranted. Should we stop wearing a particular brand of makeup because the company historically tested on animals? When looking at issues like this it is always best to consider 'the three Rs': Reduce, Refine and Replace. Could a scientific test have reduced the number of animals involved? Could it be modified in such a way that the process would cause less distress to the animal? Is there an alternative way that the results could be ascertained such as a computer model? Critical analysis such as this is vital for improving the way scientific research is carried out.

As with all ethical questions it is important that you should have your own views and opinions. The use of animals in research is an issue that will come up time and again not only during your studies as a vet, but also the rest of your professional career. Veterinary students will find that a large proportion of their pre-clinical years will involve the dissection of both fresh and fixed cadavers. There is simply no getting round this and the process is essential for not only learning anatomy but also developing fundamental surgical skills. Equally all veterinary students will spend hours looking down microscopes at fixed slides of both healthy and diseased tissue from animals. In short there is no time for someone on the course who has extreme views on the use of animals for learning.

13. **What are your thoughts on rearing animals for meat?**

This question is looking for your ability to consider both sides of the argument for and against rearing animals for food, including considering the need to maintain high welfare standards for animals whilst also acknowledging that many of your future clients make their living from rearing meat. Whatever your personal views on meat the fact is that as a future vet you will, at the least, have to train in aspects of meat production and so having extreme views will not endear you to the interviewers.

14. **How do you feel about cruelty to animals?**

Again, this question is testing your ability to examine a situation from both sides and form a well balanced and reasoned argument and suggest a carefully considered solution. Obviously, as a prospective vet you will be repulsed by the prospect of animal cruelty but it is important to acknowledge that in certain specific cases there may be reasons for apparent cruelty taking place and the interviewers will want to see what you might do in such a situation. For example, what would you do if you visited a farm and felt that the farmer was keeping the livestock in poor condition? Would you immediately report them to the RSPCA or try to perhaps talk things over with a colleague and maybe tactfully suggest improvements to the farmer? There is no real right or wrong answer to such a scenario and the interviewers will rather be looking at how you think about and put together your argument.

15. **What is your opinion of veterinary TV Programmes?**

An increasing amount of UK television scheduling is being devoted to following vets both domestically and abroad. It is also a fairly safe assumption that many people applying to vet school were influenced by such programmes. Whether it was old repeats of All Creatures Great and Small, Rolf Harris and Animal Hospital, or following the trials and tribulations of the Bristol vets from the BBC shows Vet School and Vets in Practice, and the most recent show Super Vets, it is true that many TV vets are now household names. Certainly one could argue that programmes such as Super Vets allows a whole generation of wannabe vets to see complex procedures being carried out and gain some insight into veterinary as a career. However, is the placing of a pacemaker in a dog an entirely realistic expectation of what an average vet's normal working day could involve? Equally whilst programmes following zoo vets or those working with large game in Africa are fascinating, they represent an incredibly small proportion of the profession. Some could argue therefore that such shows only act to provide a skewed view of what being a vet involves and may result in applicants having wholly unreasonable expectations of what their job may actually entail. This, however, is obviously another reason why relevant work experience is so important.

Another interesting point is the amount of time that some of these programmes dedicate to the non-professional side of the characters they follow. Whilst the love life of your colleagues and peers may be something you follow with great interest, is depicting this side of members of the profession an entirely educational experience for the viewer. Often scenes in vet docu-soaps will be highly emotive, with dramatic music underscoring the breaking of sad news. Frequently this is preceded by the off-screen director asking if the animal is likely to die. Whilst death is an unavoidable side of a vet's working life, the chances of a cat dying during a routine castrate are relatively slim, and shrewd viewers should be aware of when the show's producer is trying to make the most mundane part of the job seem more exciting for the benefit of providing drama and entertainment for those watching at home.

Watching vet TV programmes may be informative but they are not nearly as educational as spending time gaining work experience doing the real thing. A thirty minute show may be packed with excitement and drama from beginning to end, but this is rarely a true reflection of actual practice. No one is interested in watching a mundane afternoon block of consults, yet these make up almost every day of the average vet in practice. Often money, which is a hugely important factor in deciding the final choice of treatment for a beloved pet or farm animal, is overlooked completely. So whilst you may be basing your entire future career on the lovely Trude Mostue, be aware that you really can't believe everything you see on TV. At the end of the day there is no better experience than seeing vets working first hand.

16. **What can you tell me about emerging diseases in animals and PETS?**

With climate change and an increase in the number of pets being taken on holiday with their owners it was only a matter of time before we started to see new diseases presenting in the UK. An example is the parasite *Angiostrongylus vasorum*, otherwise known as the French heartworm. The adult worms of this species live in the right ventricle (one of the chambers) of the heart as well as the pulmonary (lung) arteries. The eggs they lay hatch very rapidly and the young larvae cross the alveoli of the lungs. This results in the host animal coughing up the larvae and then swallowing them. They then pass through the gut and are passed out in the faeces. For their complete development *A.vasorum* need to spend a proportion of their life-cycle within an intermediate host, choosing either slugs or snails. If a dog eats an infected slug or snail they will then pick up the worms which will travel to the heart of the animal and repeat the cycle.

In areas where the parasite is endemic, foxes act as a reservoir of infection, although at present it is unclear as to whether the whole parasite lifecycle occurs independently to dogs.

As can be expected, the clinical signs associated with the infection reflect the location that the adult worms live within the dog.

Damage to the lungs may result in difficulties breathing, coughing and haemoptysis (coughing up blood). A decrease in blood supply to the lungs as a result of a blocked right ventricle will present as lethargy and fainting. The worm also affects normal blood clotting which may result in excess bruising (although this may be difficult to visualise), bleeding disorders, and neurological symptoms if a bleed occurs in the central nervous system. Poor growth, lameness, diarrhoea and blindness have all been associated with *A. vasorum* infection.

Treatment is difficult as the dog may have an allergic reaction to the worms once they have been killed by an anthelmintic drug. Infected animals will often require adjunctive therapies to support any respiratory or cardiovascular (heart) disease, including being given antibiotics and extra oxygen.

The example of *A.vasorum* makes the point that there are a number of diseases and parasites that are not normally seen in animals in the UK but with climate change and the increased travel of animals the risks of these diseases being introduced is increasing. It is with the aim of protecting the UK that the pet passport scheme was introduced (see below).

Other important diseases to be aware of that may be introduced to the UK by pets travelling back into the UK are:

1. **Rabies** – this is endemic in many European countries and is one of the diseases that any pet wishing to re-enter the UK from Europe must be vaccinated against.

2. **Leishmaniasis** – this is a protozoal disease that is spread by biting sandflies, and is endemic in a number of Mediterranean countries. The parasite enters the animal's bloodstream by infecting macrophages, a type of white blood cell, and can then spread to various organs in the body, including the skin, where they can

cause a range of symptoms. Any animal presented to a vet with suspected infectious disease and with a history of prior travel, even if several years before, should have Leishmaniasis considered as a possible differential. The most effective way to protect pets against contracting Leishmaniasis is to avoid sandfly bites by both minimising time spent in areas with sandflies, especially at dusk when the flies tend to be most active, and treating animals with insecticides.

3. *Echinococcus multilocularis* – this is a tapeworm that dogs and cats, which are both examples of definitive hosts, contract by eating infected meat. It causes relatively little disease in dogs and cats in whom the worms attach to the lining of the gut where they produce eggs. If these eggs, which are present in the animal's faeces, are accidentally eaten by an intermediate host, including humans, then they can cause something called 'hydatid disease.' The parasite invades the bloodstream and travels to the liver where cysts are formed. They can also spread to other organs including the brain. These cysts grow and invade surrounding tissue, resembling a highly invasive and aggressive cancer. As a result it is an important example of a zoonosis and taken very seriously.

A zoonosis is a disease that normally infects animals but which can also infect humans. Zoonotic diseases are therefore of great importance and a lot of research and effort is directed to protecting humans from them. To this end vets play an incredibly important role.

PETS (Pet Travel Scheme)
This was established in 2000 for cats and dogs travelling from certain EU countries into the UK. It was later extended to include several other countries, including non-EU places like mainland USA, Canada and Bahrain, and also to include pet ferrets. The purpose of PETS is to protect the UK against the introduction of rabies and other specific diseases. Dogs, cats and ferrets travelling back in to the UK under PETS need to satisfy certain requirements

in order to avoid having to complete six months quarantine. These requirements are:

1. Animals must be **microchipped** before any other stage of the process and the number recorded.
2. Any dog, cat or ferret entering the UK must be **vaccinated against rabies**. This can be done once the animal has been microchipped so that easy identification can be achieved.
3. Twenty-one days after the last rabies vaccine is given a **blood sample** is taken so that antibody levels against rabies can be tested. If the levels are equal to or greater than a specific level then a certificate is issued and an authorised veterinary surgeon can then issue the animal with a pet passport.

It is important to note that although animals can leave the UK once vaccinated, they are unable to re-enter until 6 months has lapsed from the date that the blood test yielding a satisfactory rabies titre was taken.

Rabies vaccination needs to be boosted according to the specific vaccine manufacturer's datasheet and it is important to keep any animal up to date as lapsing, even by a day, will mean that vaccination and blood testing needs to be repeated.

4. Pets must be **treated against tapeworm and ticks** 24 to 48 hours before re-entering the UK, and this has to be completed and certified by a vet.
5. Animals must travel with an approved transport company on an authorised route.

It is important to note that it is the owner's responsibility to check the specific requirements for travel of their pet to individual countries and to ensure that all paperwork is up to date.

For more detailed information on PETS readers are directed to the DEFRA website (www.defra.gov.uk).

17. What can you tell me about Avian Influenza?

Avian Influenza (AI), or Bird Flu as it is commonly known, is caused by a type A influenza virus. It primarily affects the respiratory, nervous and digestive systems. Highly Pathogenic Avian Influenza (HPAI) is lethal and causes large losses of production birds. An outbreak of HPAI results in the disruption or cessation of national and international trade. Avian Influenza H5N1 is an example of a strain of the virus that is capable of causing potentially fatal respiratory disease in humans if they come into close contact with infected birds.

On the 3rd February 2007, a poultry farm in Suffolk was confirmed as having highly pathogenic H5N1 Avian Influenza in its flock. A 3km Protection Zone and 10km Surveillance Zone were immediately enforced and a humane cull of the 159,000 birds carried out. More recently, in early 2008, wild swans in Dorset were found to be infected with H5N1 AI. Ten swans within the Protection Zone were found to have the disease, but there was no further evidence of spread into other birds within the area.

The reason that so much media attention is directed towards AI is due to its zoonotic potential. Influenza is a virus that mutates regularly and it is a major concern that it will develop the ability to spread directly from human to human with the risk of it causing a global influenza pandemic similar to that seen in 1918. Currently only humans who have been in very close contact with sick or dead birds have contracted the disease. However, if the virus were to acquire genes from the human influenza virus, the chances of human to human spread are greatly increased. Looking at cases in both Thailand and Vietnam, where there have been human fatalities, it appears that H5N1 is resistant against two out the four currently available antiviral drugs, although it is believed that the two remaining drugs would be effective in an outbreak.

It is still widely believed that a pandemic of human influenza from an avian virus is likely. However, there is strong optimism that effective culling and response to outbreaks of AI (such as in Hong

Kong in 1997, when the entire poultry population was culled within 3 days) will avert a human pandemic.

18. **What do you know about Bluetongue?**

A relatively new disease to the UK and still very topical is Bluetongue. This viral disease infects both cattle and sheep. What makes this particular virus interesting is that it is unable to pass directly between individuals, instead requiring the culicoides midge to play an important role in the disease lifecycle.

The first cases in the UK were officially reported in East Anglia by DEFRA on the 28th September 2007. Since then the disease has spread throughout the South East and Norfolk.

Sheep are particularly susceptible to the disease with up to a 70% mortality rate in infected individuals. Cows usually show far fewer clinical signs and instead act as a reservoir for the virus. The disease presents with symptoms similar to another important notifiable disease, Foot and Mouth, due to it primarily affecting both the hooves and mouth of affected individuals. The oral mucosa (lining of the mouth) may appear red and inflamed, with areas of ulceration, erosion and necrosis. The face and neck become swollen and the animal may appear lame due to inflammation of the feet. Clinically infected individuals develop a high fever, difficulty breathing and produce a clear discharge from the eyes and nose which becomes more purulent (snotty) with time. Pregnant animals will often abort, and those which recover may be left sterile and so unable to be bred from again. Interestingly the blue cyanotic tongue that gives the disease its name is a fairly rare phenomenon.

Midges chew the skin of their hosts, rupturing blood vessels, and feeding off the blood pool that develops. If this contains bluetongue virus they will then ingest it. The virus must then undergo a period of replication within the midge. This requires high temperatures for up to 10 days. At this point the virus will be present in the saliva of the midge, and subsequent bites to cattle or sheep will pass the disease on. A single bite from an infected midge is all that is required. Midges will preferentially feed on cattle although will bite sheep if there are no cows available.

During the winter months, when the adult culicoides midge is unable to survive, Bluetongue virus hides in an inactive state within the immune cells of cattle. The virus is then activated by midge saliva the following summer if the carrier animal is bitten. Further bites result in midges becoming infected and thus able to spread the disease on to more livestock. Whilst midges themselves are only able to fly short distances, they may be carried for many miles by the wind.

An outbreak of the disease would result in the restriction of live export of sheep and cattle from this country. At present DEFRA enforces movement restrictions around any premises with confirmed bluetongue to try and halt the spread of the disease. Farmers receive compensation for animals culled in an effort to prevent further spread of Bluetongue but not for animals killed for welfare reasons associated with the disease. Vaccination is currently underway in the UK in areas where further outbreaks of Bluetongue are likely. However, the vaccine is specific to certain strains, and thus would be ineffective against different forms of the disease. Also, whilst the vaccine may be effective at preventing clinical disease, it may not give full protection and will thus allow the development of carrier individuals.

Bluetongue is an excellent example of a new disease of animals that has arrived in the UK due to climate change. Similar diseases such as African Horse Sickness may follow soon and will present considerable challenges to both vets and those who keep animals.

19. What do you know about bovine tuberculosis?

Tuberculosis is an important disease with respect to cattle. As a zoonosis it is a potential source of disease in humans. The testing, prevention, compensation and research into TB costs the government £99 million pounds a year and is therefore a large burden on the taxpayer. The disease in cattle is caused by a bacterium, *Mycobacterium bovis*. The disease results in a cough, weight loss and potential diarrhoea in affected individuals, with skin and mammary forms of the disease also possible.

Infected milk was the main source of infection in humans in the 1950s, with around 2500 deaths per annum. Pasteurisation of milk has decreased infections by 99%. There are still occasional cases of human bovine TB, predominantly in those who work in close proximity to cattle, especially abattoir and farm workers. Cases are particularly common in immune-suppressed individuals.

It is important to have an accurate method of detecting the disease. It is difficult to culture the bacteria and a rising level of antibodies may not be seen until a long time after the initial infection. The method currently being used involves looking at the cellular immune response. Not only is this strong but occurs fairly rapidly after initial infection (3-4 weeks). A sample of protein, known as tuberculin, is extracted from *M.bovis* and *M.avium* (tuberculosis from birds). These are injected into an area of clipped skin on the neck in two different sites. Special callipers are used to measure the thickness of the skin. After 72 hours the measurements of skin thickness are taken again. The frequency of the compulsory testing depends on the area that the farm is in, with geographical regions showing high incidence of the disease requiring more regular testing.

Cattle that are positive for bovine TB (bTB) are required to be culled by the State Veterinary Service. Farmers receive compensation for these animals. Milk from individuals that react to the tuberculin test must not be used for human consumption and cannot enter the bulk tank. Movement of livestock on and off the farm is halted, except for animals being sent for slaughter. Before the rest of the animals on the farm can be moved, the herd has to undergo stringent re-testing sixty days after the initial positive result. followed by a further sixty days. During this period, when a herd has lost its official TB free status, the milk must be heat treated before being allowed to be sold for human consumption. Farmers should be warned not to drink unpasteurised milk to avoid contracting TB themselves. If all the cattle test as negative, movement restrictions are lifted and the cattle are declared TB free. After six months the cows will be tested again to ensure they are still clear.

At present a new test, the BOVIGRAM interferon-gamma test, is routinely used in New Zealand. Skin testing still remains the main method for testing in this country, although the new test can be used in conjunction.

Badgers are often implicated in the spread of bovine tuberculosis. One of the largest studies into the relationship between badgers and the spread of TB was the Krebs Review. This long term study looked at the effect of culling badgers in certain areas on the prevalence of TB in cattle. There is a proven high prevalence of TB in areas with large badger populations. Culling of badgers resulted in a decreased incidence of TB in an area, although a concurrent rise in adjoining areas was observed. Farmers can take practical steps in decreasing the attractiveness of their farm to badgers. Cattle feed should be stored safely. Farmers should particularly be aware of where active sets and badger latrines are, and thus keep cattle away from these. They should also be careful where they buy their new stock from and be sure of the TB status of those farms.

20. Tell me about antibiotic/ anthelmintic resistance.

Antibiotics and anthelmintics are both examples of chemotherapeutic agents. Antibiotics are used in the treatment of bacterial infections whilst anthelmintics are the drugs of choice for use against parasitic infection. Combined, these drugs represent the bulk of vets' repertoire of treatment options. Both of these drug classes have revolutionised veterinary medicine, no less so than with respect to farming. Widespread use of these drugs allowed farmers to intensify their farming methods, enabling them to keep more stock in less space, whilst being able to prevent the normal bacterial and parasitic infections that these practices promote. Antibiotics were even added in low quantities to feed as growth promoters.

However, low levels of antibiotics fed like this are an excellent way to promote resistance to that particular drug. Likewise, inappropriate overuse of anthelmintics has resulted in widespread resistance. Resistance can be defined as when there are a greater number of individuals (worms or bacteria) within a population that are able to tolerate doses of a compound compared to a normal population of the same species. This resistance must also be a characteristic that can be inherited by the offspring of the bacterium or parasite.

It is important that the antibiotic reaches the site of infection at a high enough dose. Therefore the location of infection will dictate the type of antibiotic used and the route of administration, for example, in tablet form or injection. It is vital that the drugs are used for a long enough time period to ensure that all of the bacteria have been killed. This is an excellent example of why good communication skills are vital in a veterinary surgeon. It is essential to clearly explain how often and for how long drugs should be administered, irrespective of whether the owner thinks their pet is back to full health sooner than the end of the course. Failure to do so may result in the survival of resistant organisms. If possible, growing the bugs that are causing the disease, and then testing them to find the most suitable antibiotic is the gold standard. Dual therapy can also be considered, attacking bacteria in two different ways, by two different types of antibiotic. By doing this, the formation of resistance to one of the antibiotics will not promote survival of resistant bacteria, as they will be killed by the other drug. An example of this treatment is the use of 'PenStrep,' which is a penicillin and an aminoglycoside combined in one treatment.

Currently one in seven cases of human TB are totally resistant to all known antibiotics. There is also now a strain of cholera resistant to all antibiotics except tetracycline. You cannot watch the news without hearing of new cases of MRSA or *C.difficile* outbreaks within hospitals. However, these bacteria are not confined to just human medicine and there are an increasing number of veterinary hospitals reporting cases of these 'superbugs'.

At present there are three major groups of anthelmintics we can use in the treatment of parasites: Macrocyclic Lactones (ML); Benzimidazoles (BZ); and Levamisoles (LEV). At present there is 96% resistance to ML and around 80% resistance to BZ on all New Zealand cattle farms. In Australia there is widespread resistance to all three groups whilst in Scotland we saw the UK's first closure of a sheep farm due to resistance to all groups of anthelmintics. Similar reports have also come from Devon. Goats are particularly susceptible to resistant parasites and as long ago as 1996, herds in Devon and Somerset were showing triple resistance. Unlike antibiotics, the rules governing the sale of anthelmintics are not as strict. Therefore farmers are able to buy these drugs, and may use them inappropriately, furthering the development of resistant parasites. An excellent example of inappropriate use is misjudging the body weight of a livestock animal and underdosing, the result being that not all the parasites within the animal are killed. A practical approach would be to find the heaviest animal in the flock and dose according to that animal's weight.

There are currently schemes in operation to try and educate users in the appropriate use of these drugs against parasites. One of the most important is the Sustainable Control of Parasites in Sheep (SCOPS) scheme. For more information on this and the various techniques that farmers can apply in the appropriate control of parasites you can visit the National Sheep Association's website: *www.nationalsheep.org.uk.*

As a sobering thought it can take in excess of fifteen years to develop a new antibiotic from initial conception to clinical use. Bacteria are able to form resistance in as little as three weeks. It is therefore of utmost importance that antibiotics and anthelmintics are used appropriately. Of equal importance are vets who enter research and develop the new chemotherapeutic agents that we can use in the constant fight against bacterial and parasitic infections.

Which vet school should I choose?

When it comes to making a decision on which vet school to accept an offer from the chances are that your options will be limited by which of the schools actually make you an offer. After all, if only one vet school makes you an offer then there won't really be a huge amount of pondering for you to do! If, however, you are one of those candidates fortunate enough to receive more than one offer then the decision making process will depend on a number of factors. These include:

ACADEMIC

1. The grade offers made – if you really aren't that bothered about which of the schools you go to and have a couple of offers but with differing grades then some would argue that it makes more sense to accept the lower grade offer so that if you don't do quite as well in your exams as you'd hoped then you'll still be able to accept the place. Of course, others would argue that it makes as much sense to accept the higher grade offer as your first choice with the lower offer as your insurance so that if you don't make the grades to accept your first choice you can hopefully 'cash in' on your insurance place. Both methods operate on essentially the same principle.

2. The course structure – with the exception of the new course at Nottingham most of the schools run essentially similar courses in terms of their structure, with the first two years covering pre-clinical aspects of your training, the third being para-clinical in nature, and the final two years clinical. There will be more detail on each of these phases a little later in the chapter. As such, decisions made on the basis of course structure and content will probably be made on more subtle features as the amount of self-directed learning, or the resources available to you for out-of-lecture learning. The reputation of the lecturers may also be an important factor for you in making a decision although most students will be less concerned with these considerations and more so with aspects of university life such as the reputation of the student union or the number and type of societies available, as well as the character of the individual city.

3. The year size – if you are fortunate enough to have a number of offers and are trying to separate the schools out then class size may be a deciding factor as there are some differences between them. Cambridge still has the smallest year sizes, with London having an annual intake of about 270 students. The average year size appears to be around the 120 students mark and unless you really have a deep desire to avoid a large year then the chances are that this factor won't be of any concern.

4. Extra-mural studies (EMS) – all veterinary students have to complete a specific number of weeks of practice outside of the course hours to satisfy the Royal College of Veterinary Surgeons' requirements before graduation. Some vet schools leave students to arrange these placements themselves whilst others handle the organisation in-house. There are pros and cons to each system and it is worth asking each of the schools how they manage EMS.

NON-ACADEMIC

1. Geography – if you want to study relatively close to home so that you are able to pop back easily at weekends or during the holidays then it probably wouldn't make much sense to accept an offer at a university the opposite end of the country if you also have one from a closer school. It's all very well thinking that you'd happily get as far away from your annoying family as you can but it's amazing how strong the pull of home can sometimes be, especially during the latter stages of the course when the pressure starts mounting. It's also worth mentioning that most student halls, assuming you live in them during your first year, either use your room, and therefore need you out of them, or charge extra for use during university holidays. As such, choosing a university within a relatively sensible distance from home makes sense unless you relish the challenge of lugging all of your worldly possessions back with you on the train. We know we wouldn't. Having said all this, if you only receive one offer then screw the distance and take the offer – you can always get a student rail-card!

2. Leisure and Hobbies – we touched upon this during the applications chapter. Your choice of university to accept an offer from may be guided by the hobbies you have and therefore the amenities that the individual university may offer. Super-keen on extreme mountain-biking or climbing? Well, perhaps Cambridge wouldn't be the greatest choice. To be fair, most universities will have clubs and societies catering to most hobbies and interests and if your particular leisure activity involves travelling further afield than the city then most places within the UK are fairly easily reached from most other places so, again, this particular consideration isn't really as important in the grand scheme of things. If you do want to climb then you'll be able to do so just as easily in London or Nottingham as you would in Glasgow. If, however, you really can't live without missing a single weekend of scuba-diving coral reefs then maybe, just maybe, St Georges is your preferred destination!

3. Weather – yes, that's right. We're actually suggesting that weather might play a role in your ultimate decision because let's be honest if you were to actually research the weather in each of the vet school cities there would likely be a difference between them. We're only suggesting it – you will need to make up your own mind as to whether this is an important factor for you.

4. Culture – Thankfully the universities that boast vet schools are for the most part in cities which offer rich cultural offerings from art to theatre to interesting architecture. This one probably really requires you to have visited the city to judge for yourself whether the cultural offerings are what you're looking for.

Whichever university you accept an offer from and attend the likelihood is that you'll have an amazing time and come away convinced that you made the best choice, which of course you did. No matter where you study, university and vet school in particular is an incredible experience and one which will stay with you for the rest of your life.

Basic Course Structure

As already mentioned, most of the courses offered by the UK vet schools are broadly similar, owing mainly to the fact that they have to comply with the requirements of the RCVS. Most differences will tend to come towards the end of the degree, in the clinical area. The basic breakdown is as follows:

a) Pre-Clinical – this covers the first two years of the course and involves studying aspects of normal animal physiology, anatomy and husbandry. Subjects covered will also include biochemistry which at first may not seem very relevant. The important thing to remember is that the initial years are providing you with the firm scientific grounding and base knowledge that will then enable the clinical stages of the course to make sense. This is always worth keeping in the back of your mind when you're trying to write that last-minute essay on sodium channels at 4am! The pre-clinical years will comprise a mixture of lectures, small group tutorials, laboratory practicals ('labs'), DSE or coursework which may be either group based or individual, and animal handling practicals. Often the hardest thing to get used to is taking notes in lectures, as most of us will be used to the school method of teaching whereby we are taught in much smaller classes and there is regular checking of understanding from the teachers. At university lecturers will come in, start talking and, save for the occasional interruption to clarify a point or two, will lecture without stopping for forty-five minutes to an hour and then leave, perhaps after taking a few questions from some students at the front. The pace of lectures is generally much faster than school lessons and you will rapidly develop your own system for taking legible, detailed notes that will be comprehensible come revision time. We were implored in our first lecture NOT to go home and try to rewrite our lecture notes neatly as we would burn out after one term. This is certainly true and it soon becomes clear that because you are so busy at all times it is vital to learn to take good notes. Any additional work outside of lectures should aim to supplement and not repeat the material covered in lectures, which is generally the 'core' material and which, if learned for exams, would result in a pass. The additional reading around a subject that you may or may not choose to do is the knowledge that will then be expected to move you into the merit and distinction categories at examination time.

The main subjects commonly covered during the pre-clinical years are:

1. Veterinary anatomy – this may include lectures, coursework, tutorials, practical dissection sessions and histology classes, as well as computer-aided teaching and live anatomy. The aim is to study the normal, healthy animal and will focus principally on the main veterinary species – dog, cat, horse and farm species – with modules on exotics.

2. Veterinary physiology – this examines how the various organ systems and biological processes function and interact in the healthy animal, thus providing an excellent grounding from which to then examine pathology and medicine.

3. Biochemistry – as with physiology this examines how biological systems function at the cellular and sub-cellular level and provides a basis for later study of pharmacology.

4. Animal Health and Husbandry (name may vary) – this subject provides the 'vet' aspects of the first two years and is what most students enjoy the most. Subjects studied tend to include farming systems, housing, genetics, feeding systems and general animal handling and husbandry systems. This subject will provide the majority of the animal handling opportunities in the first couple of years.

b) Para-Clinical – this stage follows on from the pre-clinical phase by introducing aspects of pathology and we start to look at what happens when things go wrong in animals. As such, this is the year to two years which provide the stepping stone or link to the clinical stage of the course and transform you from an accomplished scientist and academic into a competent clinician. The para-clinical subjects are taught in much the same manner as the pre-clinical subjects and normally include the following subjects:

1. Pathology – this is the study of disease and abnormal structure and function of biological systems. It soon becomes clear why time was spent studying normal anatomy and physiology earlier in the course when you start pathology as the abnormal is so much easier to get your head around when you can compare it the normal state.

2. Parasitology – a lot of a vet's work is involved in preventing and treating disease caused by parasites, both external and internal, and understanding the role parasites play in wider disease transmission and pathogenesis. As such it is vital to have a good understanding of parasite structure and life cycles so that we can better understand the measures at our disposal to control them.

3. Pharmacology – vets use a lot of drugs. This is no reference to their social lives of course but rather to the wide range of medicines we have available for use in treating disease. It is vital that we understand how medicines work if we are to be allowed to prescribe them and administer them to patients. This means studying their effects at the sub-cellular level and also having an in-depth appreciation of their potential side-effects and pharmocodynamics (how they distribute and are processed by the body). This subject is the one where it becomes clear why biochemistry was studied earlier in the course as it builds upon a good understanding of biochemical principles.

4. Microbiology – bacteria, viruses, fungi, and a host of slightly more unusual microorganisms are what we spend the vast majority of our professional, clinical lives battling and so it is essential that we understand how our nemeses function so that we can effectively combat them.

5. Basic clinical sciences – this subject introduces you to the subjects and skills that will end up becoming a routine part of your clinical lives. Topics such as surgical principles, anaesthesia, suture materials and techniques, and a host of other clinically relevant subjects are studied as part of this, which, depending on the vet school, may have a different title.

c) Clinical – It is the clinical stage of the course that students look forward to the most, and for good reason as it is the final stage in your training which aims to transform you from a bright young scientist into a skilled, empathetic, thoughtful veterinary surgeon ready to be let loose on the unsuspecting animals of the world. The penultimate year is, in most schools, predominantly lecture based and subjects taught include medicine, surgery and a number of other clinically relevant subjects. Needless to say the year is intense and it can often feel like you're being expected to learn the entire body of global veterinary knowledge in two terms. Most schools now have their final written examinations at the end of fourth year such that students enter the clinical final year having thoroughly revised all of the clinical lecture material and so are theoretically able to hit the clinical floor running. Although students start their rotations familiar with clinical knowledge it is most certainly the final year rotations that serve to consolidate the most important skills and knowledge. The over-riding aim of the clinical stage of the veterinary training is 'integration,' whereby all of the previously studied subjects and knowledge are drawn upon to fully understand, work-up, treat and manage a whole host of clinical scenarios. It is the stage where rote-learning has to give way to considered thinking as every case you see is unique and every day is different.

VPH (Veterinary Public Health) is an important part of the course at all of the vet schools, with all of them making efforts to increase the content of their courses. It is concerned with teaching undergraduates about the important role that vets play in ensuring food hygiene and safety at all stages in the food production process. The subject is, typically, introduced in the fourth year with teaching and examinations taking place throughout fourth and final year. Having a good knowledge of the role that vets play in upholding and promoting public health will stand you in good stead when it comes to applying to vet school as it will be evident that you have considered the many different career paths that are open to vets.

Final Year – As a Senior Veterinary Student, or final year, you will be placed into rotation groups and spend the year cycling through weeks spent in one particular department or focusing on one particular aspect of clinical veterinary science, such as laboratory medicine or public health. The focus is on how you work with your peers/ colleagues, and the clinicians and how you manage your own cases with every aspect of your approach to a case being observed and assessed. The clinical stage of the course is generally completed at the vet school's field station where the small animal, equine and large animal departments are located. The field stations for each of the UK vet schools are listed briefly below, with additional notes if any of the final year is spent studying elsewhere:

London – Hawkshead Campus (Potters Bar, Hertfordshire). Students also have the opportunity to spend time seeing clinical practice at the Beaumont Animals' Hospital (small animal) in Camden (London)

Cambridge – The Queen's Veterinary School Hospital. This is on the outskirts of the historic centre and only a short cycle ride from most of the colleges.

Bristol – Langford (near Bristol Airport).

Liverpool – Leahurst Campus (Neston, approx 15miles outside of Liverpool). Some small animal work is also done at the Fern Grove practice in Liverpool city centre.

Glasgow – Bearsden Campus (Glasgow).

Edinburgh – Easter Bush Campus (Roslin, Midlothian).

Nottingham – at the time of writing no students were yet going through the clinical stages of the course, although we believe that clinical teaching will be carried out through accredited practices in the surrounding and wider   area.

Most students will live out near the field stations during the final two years and most agree that the change in surroundings and lifestyle from the big city (Glasgow is the exception as the entire course is taught at the same site) to a more rural setting is refreshing. One of the most enjoyable aspects of the final year, other than having contact with clients and their animals, is that you get to work closely with some of the finest minds in veterinary science and will often find yourself socialising with the same clinicians and lecturers that you have been trained by for the past four years. The final year is undoubtedly tough, with some rotations and especially on-call and night-duties sometimes proving plain hellish, but it is also a very enjoyable year with the rate of learning rapid and the change you see in both yourself and other members of your year being massive. It literally is the year in which you turn from a pre-clinical caterpillar into a clinical butterfly!

Needless to say the final year is a very practical twelve months and a range of skills are learnt, or more likely improved having already been exposed to most clinical techniques during EMS placements. Such skills and clinical exposure include the following:

1. Imaging:
Radiography – taking and interpreting x-rays.

Ultrasonography – a very useful imaging technique employed in the investigation of everything from pregnancy diagnosis to equine tendon visualisation and assessment. Ultrasound uses high frequency sound waves to visualise tissues – think of pregnancy scans in humans.

MRI, CT and nuclear imaging – these advanced imaging techniques are becoming more and more widely used in practice and it is likely that you will be involved in cases that call upon their use

2. Surgery:
From referral soft tissue cases to routine neutering, and elective orthopaedic procedures to emergency fracture repairs the range of potential surgical cases you will be exposed to is huge.

3. Medicine and Intensive Care:
One week you may be on night shifts in the Intensive Care Unit (ICU), monitoring critically ill patients and administering life-saving medicines with the next spent working closely with a pre-eminent canine internal medicine specialist seeing referral medicine cases. Again, the range of potential cases and learning experiences is virtually limitless.

4. Small Animal:
From managing referral cases one rotation to seeing first opinion cases as a 'GP' vet the next students rapidly develop not only important clinical skills from thoracic and cardiac auscultation to advising on options for flea and worm treatment but also hone those vital communication skills.

5. Large Animal:
Routine foot trimming to out of hours calvings and treating 'downer cows' followed up, perhaps, by a project investigating a herd's drop in milk yield means that farm animal rotations lead to the development of first class

investigative skills and with large animals it is vitally important to become adept at animal handling. Pregnancy diagnosis by rectal palpation – the classic veterinary image – and ultrasound is one area in which most students see a huge change in themselves as they go from feeling "mush" to accurately diagnosing early pregnancy and assessing ovaries.

6. Equine:
Lameness assessment and the exhilarative stress of receiving, triaging and managing a surgical case of colic at one in the morning are examples of the type of cases seen during equine work. As well as managing hospital-based cases there is also time spent honing general practice skills whilst out on the road with clinicians visiting first-opinion and routine cases.

An entire book could be written – and maybe it will – on the plethora of case types and experiences that a final year veterinary student will potentially be exposed to during the closing stages of their training and we advise trying to get friendly with one if you want to find out more as the best way to get the most useful information is to get it directly from the 'horse's mouth.'

EMS (Extra-Mural Studies)
The above is basically a fancy term for compulsory practical experience. In order to become a member of the Royal College of Veterinary Surgeons and receive the letters MRCVS after your name students must satisfy the RCVS that they have achieved a minimum level of practical experience with the main species and in the main areas of clinical activity. The RCVS have relatively general requirements and each of the vet schools may interpret them in slightly different ways. However, a good general overview is as follows:

1. Pre-clinical (must be completed, certified and signed off by the vet school before entering the third year): 3 weeks of two types and 2 weeks each of the rest of dairy, pig, equine, small animal practice (with the emphasis being on shadowing and understanding the role of nurses within the practice), and lambing. The total number of weeks that need to be signed off is twelve.

2. Clinical (must be completed, certified and signed off before graduation, with most students either completing their EMS during the Christmas or Easter directly preceding the final exams in the summer): a total of 26 weeks must be completed with time spent seeing clinical practice in small animals, both referral and first opinion, large animals and equine. A compulsory week spent engaged in experience of veterinary public health work is also required as part of the Veterinary Public Health teaching. This could take the form of time spent working with an OV (Official Veterinarian) in an abattoir or other forms of placement. Due to the number of weeks that have to be completed there is very little spare time during vacations in both fourth and final year and as such the two years prove to be extremely busy. This is one of the issues that places pressure on the finances of vet students and will be discussed in the later chapter on funding.

It is worth mentioning that the RCVS are, at the time of print, starting a review of EMS requirements, so things may change in future years.

St George's, Grenada

This University trains both veterinary and medical students on a beautiful Caribbean island such that a typical day could see you receiving lectures in soft tissue surgical techniques in the morning and snorkelling in picture postcard settings in the afternoon. The training is similar in nature to that provided at Nottingham, with the dean of St George's having been involved in the establishment and design of the Nottingham course. As such there is a lot of emphasis on developing real practical clinical skills from day one and studying veterinary medical principles through the use of problem-based teaching. The final, clinical, year of the course sees students completing clinical rotations in either the US if they have plans to sit the American National Veterinary Licensing examination to practice in America, or at one of the UK AVMA-accredited veterinary schools if they plan to sit the RCVS exams to become MRCVS. The school at St Georges' boasts a number of very respected and venerable specialists as visiting lecturers and the quality of teaching is well renowned. The only drawback, of course, is that students need to sit separate exams on graduation if they then want to go on and practice, with a pass in these exams certainly not guaranteed. For more information on the course and studying at St George's see the website, the address for which is given in the appendix.

Life as a Vet Student

What happens once you're actually at vet school then? What is that initial year really like and what is the 'culture' of veterinary school. Vet school is unique and in many respects very different to a 'typical' student experience. For a start it is a long course compared to the majority of degree programmes, which are usually between three to four years in length. As such vet students get to know their year very well, as well as developing a real sense of home in their respective city. In fact many students upon graduation choose to stay in the immediate area in and around their vet school's city during their first job. One other aspect of the length of the vet course that can seem strange is the fact that those non-vet friends you make during your first one to two years, especially if you go to one of the schools that are part of the wider university, graduate and leave before you. This tends to happen at about the third year stage and can mark the transition from preclinical to the clinical stage of the course and a general increase in the level of 'vettiness' that your life involves. It does seem bizarre when those friends are out in the world of work and starting careers whilst you are still studying and living the student lifestyle.

Studying veterinary medicine is intense, no doubt about it but this is certainly not a bad thing. There may not be as much free time available to indulge in as many extra-curricular activities as your non-vet friends but the bond you form with members of your year and course are often a lot stronger than in other courses as a result of spending so much time together. Chris intercalated in biochemistry and was surprised how little time members of the course actually spent with each other and as a result how some members of the year didn't even know each other. To go through three years at university and graduate without knowing everyone seemed alien and actually a little bit sad. With the vet course, unless you are incredibly insular in which case you are unlikely to have been offered a place, then there is a very good chance that you will know everyone in your year and probably in other years as well, including at other vet schools. Vet school feels a bit like a big family in that respect. Vet students are renowned for 'working hard and playing harder.' This doesn't mean that they're out getting drunk every night – after all, the course is tough and does require students to knuckle down and do some work! What it does mean is that when it is time to unwind and have fun vet students do it in style. Aside from nights out with your friends there are a cornucopia of well organised events that feature in the typical vet school calendar. For example, Bristol has both an annual soiree in the autumn term – a sort of pre-ball ball if you like – and then the big vet ball in the spring, which is always a true highlight. It's not all black ties and cocktail dresses however. There are plenty of opportunities to dress up in daft costumes whilst at university and in fact vets are masters of fancy dress, with most of us leaving university with a bigger comedy wardrobe than our normal clothes! From Christmas parties to the infamous AVS Sports Weekend we love nothing more than to pretend to be someone or something different in the name of entertainment. AVS Sports Weekend deserves a particularly special mention as it really is one of the great annual events, which sees vet students from all vet schools and all years converge on one of the UK vet school cities each autumn for a full weekend of partying, socialising and (some) sport. Each vet school has its own fancy dress theme, with the final years having their own separate theme. Previous years have seen vets go as pirates, Smurfs, Wally from Where's Wally, right the way through to Ronald McDonald! Imagine seeing two hundred Ronald McDonalds running through your city! It really is a great way to meet vet students from other schools and is something that every prospective vet should experience at least once.

Whilst vet students know how to party they are also incredibly creative and find numerous avenues for demonstrating this from writing and staging amazing pantomimes, based often on members of clinical staff, to music with a number of students forming bands. Chris actually founded and played in his own rock band during his final two years at university! Sports also plays a vital part in the lives of most vet students with numerous teams drawing upon the plethora of skills and tons of enthusiasm that vet students possess. It is actually a really great idea to get involved in sport whilst at vet school as not only is it very social but keeps you fit, an essential quality if you are to cope with the rigours of life as a working vet. It also provides a great excuse for returning occasionally to your old vet school, as demonstrated by the annual Bristol Old Boys versus New Boys rugby match which sees Bristol graduates return once a year to challenge current vet students to an epic match, followed by a cracking social.

All this fun obviously requires a lot of organisation and this is another thing that vet students are masters at. Vet student societies are present at every UK vet school and do everything from organising socials to getting sponsorship for events and deals on cheap textbooks to representing the views and concerns of students on various academic and non-academic committees. It's a lot of hard work but the feeling of really working together with fellow students to make a difference makes it all worthwhile. As well as each university having their main vet student societies and various smaller clubs, vet students have the opportunity to act on a national and even international front. AVS is the Association of Veterinary Students and is essentially the student arm of the BVA (British Veterinary Association). The Sports Weekend is just one of the many things that AVS do and they represent the views of vet students to the BVA and ultimately to Government. The annual AVS Congress is a slightly more sober but equally fun event, with interesting lectures and a great congress ball to enjoy. Check out the website (address in the appendix) for more information on what AVS are all about. IVSA, or the International Veterinary Student Association, is an organisation that brings vet students together from all over the world and is involved in a range of excellent projects and provides a fantastic opportunity to integrate with veterinary colleagues from other countries. The wonders of the internet and social networking sites also mean that it is even easier than ever before to communicate with vets and students from all corners of the globe!

Vet school feels less like a university course and honestly more like a huge extended family, with an amazing array of people, activities and incredible experiences to keep you smiling from day one until graduation and beyond. Ask any vet about their time at university and I challenge you to find one that doesn't say they were the best years of their life!

Finance

It is becoming more expensive to study to become a vet. Fact. With the abolition of the classic student grant, then the introduction of tuition fees and, most recently, the prospect of being asked to pay 'top-up' fees it is clear that the days of a 'free' university education are doomed. On the one hand this is an inevitable change and one for the greater good as it focuses students' minds on that which matters the most: a university education is an investment in one's future and not simply an opportunity to spend three years waking up at the crack of noon and graduate with an honours in 'Xbox.' Nothing does this in quite the same way as asking students to pay for their education. However, there are also drawbacks to this new age of costly tertiary education with the primary one being that graduates are racking up ever greater levels of debt upon leaving university thus leaving them to start their careers saddled with, often, huge debts and certainly delaying such important economic activities as entering the housing market. The other potential drawback, of course, is the danger of turning back the clock and rendering a university education a preserve of the wealthy. "What are vets worried about student debt for? They're going to be loaded when they start work!" This is an opinion that is levelled at vets and vet students all the time and although a career in veterinary medicine will, on the whole, not leave you living on a diet of beans and stale bread the truth is that as far as the main professions go we are certainly nowhere near being the high rollers of the world. Aside from salary issues there are a number of course-specific points to explore that go some way to highlighting the particular financial trials of studying to become a veterinary surgeon.

The Association of Veterinary Students (AVS) and British Veterinary Association (BVA) regularly conduct a survey of all veterinary students at the UK schools asking questions on a number of subjects, with one of the main subjects being the level of debt shouldered by their members. In 1996 the average final year student debt was £4,819 compared to a figure of £19,360 in 2005, and expected to be greater still since the introduction of top-up tuition fees. Even factoring in inflation this is quite a leap and neatly demonstrates the real financial challenge being faced by today's veterinary students. Sure, it's generally easy to get student loans, overdrafts and all sorts of other types of credit to fund your way through university but as with any debt this all needs to be paid off at some point. The facts are these:

1. The vet course is long – on average five years – and with tuition fees around £3,000 per year the likely tuition fee associated debt at the end of the course alone will be in the region of £15,000

2. EMS requirements during university vacations mean that the opportunity to earn money during holidays is severely restricted. It is sometimes possible to find jobs that are veterinary relevant and that can therefore serve a dual purpose of enabling students to earn much needed cash whilst satisfying EMS requirements but these are few and far between and the pay is likely to be relatively low compared with good old fashioned temping for example. As such, veterinary students are more likely to start the new university term or year relatively worse off than peers on other courses. The requirement to see practice during vacations also adds an extra, more direct, financial strain on veterinary students as it costs money to drive to placements, stay in B&B accommodation if necessary, and generally sustain oneself whilst on placements away from home. Some students can find themselves having to make round daily trips to and from a vet practice they are seeing practice with of 60 miles – this soon adds up to a hefty petrol bill and with no real 'allowance' from the vet schools or the RCVS the cost is carried solely by the student.

3. The course is busy. Very busy. Whilst it may be possible to find time during the earlier years of the course to engage in part-time employment the simple fact is that working part-time during the clinical years is virtually impossible due to commitments to rotations and the need to get through the sheer volume of academic work that is asked of veterinary students. Aside from the classic, traditional student jobs of bar-work and waiting tables it is possible to seek out more lucrative work such as tuition meaning that greater use can be made of the limited time you will have. Again, this means that veterinary students tend to finish terms and years relatively poorer than other friends. There is also a case to be made about 'fairness' and providing a 'level playing field.' What we mean by this is that those students who are less wealthy or well supported financially by parents and therefore have to supplement their income through term-

time employment end up doing so at the expense of time spent engaging in other activities such as academic work or expanding their social horizons or extra-curricular skill base. Is it fair that wealthier students have more of an opportunity to spend time studying and thus potentially graduate with a 'better' education or establish useful expanded networks through social activity whilst others have to sacrifice one aspect or the other of their university education just to pay for the course and eat? It is a debate that I am sure could rage on for hours!

4. No government funding. Medical and dental students can expect to receive NHS bursaries to help fund a large part of their training and although they are expected to then 'repay' some of this state investment in their education by working in the NHS the fact is that these professionals can expect to earn a lot more than their veterinary peers, maybe not immediately but certainly within a few years of graduating. It is true that veterinary medicine is a private medical profession and as such there is no obligation for the state to fund the education of it's future practitioners and beneficiaries. However, how many of you have private health insurance or see a non-NHS dentist? Is it fair that these medics and dentists enjoy financial support for their training for them to then go out and work in private practice? Debateable. It could be argued that vets do make a contribution to the health of the nation by, for example, monitoring and enforcing rules that protect us from zoonoses and helping to care for the health and wellbeing of the country's pets thus caring for the mental wellbeing of millions of people and, potentially, saving the NHS a fortune each year. So maybe we do deserve some state help for vet students. One thing that should be taken into account by government is the fact that vet students can't supplement their income in the same way as most other students and so we argue that allowances should be made for this when it comes to setting tuition fees, with a reduced rate of tuition charging perhaps appropriate.

The main sources of funding that veterinary students rely upon whilst at university are:

1. **Student loans**, which even if you don't need the money are worth applying for just to put in a savings account as it will generally be the 'cheapest' money you will ever be able to borrow. These are applied for

through your local education authority or student support department attached to the Council.

2. **Personal savings**. More students are making efforts to start saving for their university education at a relatively early age and many spend a Gap Year working in order to save money to be used, in part, to pay towards university.

3. **Parental contributions**. Many students are fortunate enough to receive considerable support from parents or relatives either through payment of tuition fees, housing rent, other specific expenses or generally through the provision of an allowance. Some parents will 'lend' money to their children with the expectation that it will be paid back at some point after graduation. Naturally most parents are unlikely to be found charging their kids commercial rates of interest and so this could prove to be a very cost effective way of 'borrowing' money as opposed to standard bank loans.

4. **Bank overdrafts**. The rush to attract new students to open accounts with them means that it is possible to get some really good deals when it comes to applying for a student bank account, with some banks offering fairly sizable interest free overdrafts. Often the interest free period will extend a little beyond graduation giving some time to start paying it off before interest gets charged. Try not to be seduced by the offer of gimmicky 'freebies' when looking at prospective student accounts as often the thing you really need over and beyond that free student rail card or MP3 player, that you might not even end up using that much anyway, is a decent sized overdraft, interest free of course, and a bank that you are confident are going to be easy and pleasant to deal with should you run into unforeseen difficulties whilst at university.

5. **Scholarships**. There aren't really many of these on offer for the vet course although it may be possible to apply for a scholarship with the Armed Forces. These are limited and may require you to sign up to work for them for a few years post-graduation. It may be possible to attract sponsorship for an intercalated degree and this can make an extra year's studying much more of a realistic option.

6. Student Maintenance Grants. At the time of print, students in England may be eligible to qualify for government maintenance grants if their parents earn below a certain threshold. The amount of financial support available is determined on a sliding scale according to parental income. It is also important to note that students whose parents earn below a certain amount may also be eligible to receive a higher level of student loan. The position may very well be different in Scotland, Wales and Northern Ireland and students are encouraged to contact their local education authority for further information.

Alternative sources of income – you may need to consider one or more of these if you find yourself financially stretched at university:

1. Part-time employment.
As discussed before it is perfectly possible to engage in part-time employment during term-time although you will be limited by time and the need to focus on the main reason you are at university – studying. It is also important to save time to relax as all work and no play is the sure-fire way to head to a breakdown. It is certainly worth trying to 'capitalise' on any skills you may have to enhance your earning potential and thus maximise on the use of your limited time. Personal tutoring, for example, can be a great way to earn money and will pay considerably more than traditional jobs like bartending. One friend of ours had trained previously as a dance instructor and funded her way – very lucratively – through university by teaching dance classes twice a week.

2. Entrepreneurialism.
Is there something that you enjoy doing that could also potentially earn you some extra money? For example, if you're a keen musician then perhaps forming a band at university and, if you're good enough, offering your (paid) services to functions, parties etc may be a good idea. The possibilities are really as endless as the imagination and drive that you have.

3. Hardship loans and Access funds.

These are made available by the university to those who find themselves in serious financial difficulties. This are limited in number and size and only offered in true emergencies.

As for paying back debts student loans start being paid back in April following the year in which you graduate, assuming you are earning above the threshold figure, and will be deducted automatically from your pay by your employer. The rate at which it is paid back works out to be approximately 4% of your annual salary before tax. For example, on a salary of £28,000 before tax in 2008 student loan deductions are £97 per month, or £1164 per year. With average student veterinary loan debt at graduation standing at approximately £15,000, paying it back at a rate of £1164 per year would mean nearly 13 years spent paying it back! Obviously no-one reasonably expects to stay on the same salary as they start on forever and so you can expect to gradually pay the loan back at a faster rate the more you start earning but unless you're earning a fortune in the City it is likely that it will take you a good number of years paying back those student loans. Greater university expense and larger student loans will simply mean higher repayments and/ or longer terms of repayment. Great fun. It is possible to pay more of the loan back as and when you choose if, for example, you find yourself with some 'spare' cash such as a bonus or inheritance and this will obviously help to reduce the amount of time you end up paying back the loan, eventually freeing up the money for use elsewhere. However, bear in mind that as the student loan is essentially interest free it would be more lucrative or sensible to either invest any 'spare' capital in higher yielding investments or pay off more 'expensive' debts (eg credit cards) before you make extra student loan payments. Other debts to repay following graduation include overdrafts which most banks will offer at either interest free or reduced interest levels for one to two years post-graduation. It is often a good idea to try really hard to pay these off before interest starts being charged as most will levy a fairly hefty (eg 24% APR) charge on any overdraft debt you still have.

Most universities publish examples of average living expenses for first year students on their websites and students are directed to these. As you will see being a student is an expensive affair but this shouldn't put you off. If all you have ever dreamed of being is a veterinary surgeon then go for it – money can be paid back and it's amazing how resourceful one can be when there is a firm and worthwhile objective being strived for.

How can veterinary students save money whilst at university? Well, there are a few sensible measures that you can take to avoid spending more than you really need to:

1. **Books and equipment** – avoid the temptation of going out as soon as you have a 'recommended reading' list and spending a small fortune on books that you will either be able to buy second hand from upper year students for a fraction of their new price, at a discount at one of the regular 'book sales' held during the first few weeks of term, or that you can borrow easily from the university libraries. Most veterinary textbooks are incredibly expensive, with some surgical texts, for example, being about £120! The average textbook price seems to be about £45 so it's clear that the cost of your own personal little library can very rapidly get out of control. We know members of our respective years who spent in excess of £800 on books in their first year – two words: NO NEED! A note on the book sales held by the main retailers is that they tend to be held a couple of weeks into term in order, I suspect, to weed out those students who get nervous about waiting for their books and panic, buying them at full price in the first week or two, especially when they see 'everyone' else buying new books. Play it cool, borrow from the library – it's worth getting to know how the libraries at your university operate within the first week or two as they are not only a great place to study but you will soon realise how easy it is to borrow the books you need and will get a better idea of which books, if any, you will need to buy. It is also worth getting to know how to search for journals online as these will be free to access from the libraries and will be a far more reliable reference than textbooks anyway, which are often 'out of date' by the time they are published! Those students with aspirations of graduating with honours may want to get into the habit of consulting journals for supplementary learning as it is this kind of source that will provide the distinction grade information required. The library staff, who are well worth befriending for their friendly advice, will be happy to show you how to search for books and journals. It may be worth joining one or two of the veterinary associations such as BVA or

BSAVA early in your university career as they publish excellent journals with useful articles of clinical relevance regularly and have the advantage of offering very cheap, or even free, membership for vet students so there is really nothing to lose by joining up. In fact, a large number of final years use publications such as The Veterinary Review and In Practice (published monthly by BVA) for the bulk of their revision and continue to consult such journals in practice so it's a good idea to become familiar with them early.

2. It is needless to say that as a student you will become quite adept at **bargain hunting**. Look for special offers on everything from travel tickets to 'buy one, get one free' offers at the supermarket. Used to always eating top branded food at home? Well, why not try out the cheaper (often considerably) own brand items. They often taste/ perform the same and who really cares if Henry or Tamara turn their nose up at you for using 'inferior' products – we can't all rely on a trust fund!

Most cities have a company or companies that produce 'discount books' or snap-fax style booklets crammed full of vouchers for special discounts at a number of businesses from clubs and pubs to hairdressers and restaurants. For a small fee it is often well worth investing in one of these as they could, over the course of a year, save you a small fortune.

In terms of travel, aim to organise yourself and book any planned travel as early as possible. This way it is often possible to save a lot more compared to buying tickets closer to the day of travel when prices seem to skyrocket.

3. **Lifestyle changes** – a few simple lifestyle or habit changes can also go some way to saving you money at university. Why not try making your own lunch to take to vet school, even if just for a couple of days per week, rather than eating in the local cafe every day. You will be surprised how much you save each week by making that tiny little time investment in the morning. Smoke? Well why not quit. Seriously, try. You will save loads and feel infinitely healthier for doing so. We could prattle on and offer tip after tip but the truth is that it's often the obvious, simple measures that you can probably already think of yourself that all add up to helping you save and empower you to reallocate money to more effective areas of use whilst at university.

One key skill to develop early on in your university career is that of budgeting and planning. It is a useful exercise to sit down and write out a list of your actual, or anticipated, expenses each month – include everything – and to then plan how much you will need each month to finance those expenses. It is also a great idea to review your banking arrangements regularly, for example once every two weeks, and to know what your overdraft limit is and what your current account balance is – there is nothing worse than suddenly realising you only have 50p to your name and it's only the third week of term. If you think you're going to need additional funds then plan ahead and aim to talk to your bank well in advance – you do not want to have to try and beg your bank for an extension at the twelfth hour as they will be far less sympathetic than if you spoke to them before you hit the rocks.

Another thing that is important is to actually know and appreciate your fiscal limits. This may require you to make the odd 'sacrifice' such as deciding to go to AVS and not the ball one year despite really wanting to go to both – there will always be next year. This is a tough thing to do especially if your friends are in the privileged position of being less financially constrained than you, but such is life.

Scott Kilpatrick BVM&S MRCVS

Scott graduated from Edinburgh University in 2007 and is currently busy working both for the PDSA and Vets Now in Gateshead.

"Applying to vet school was the easy part of this journey to becoming a vet. I have always wanted to be a vet... apart from being an international pop star it's the only job that has got me really excited! Getting good grades and having loads of work experience come as standard these days, it's the interview that makes the real difference. The best advice I have ever had was from my biology teacher a day before my Edinburgh interview. He said, 'the most important thing is to be memorable!' I think it was more a case of luck on the day... but my acceptance letter from Edinburgh came a few weeks later. The rest as they say is history and 6 years later I found myself facing my finals and the prospect of having to get a job!

There will always be those annoying people in your final year who have had jobs organised since the beginning of time. I think it is really important not to get too caught up in this competitive side of vet school. It is OK not to know what you want to do. Focus on passing your finals first... the rest will fall in to place. I spent much of final year toying with the idea of doing an internship. However, as time went on I realised the thought of spending another year in academia was not for me. After finals I wanted to go on holiday and never come back. I found myself graduating with no real plans at all.

I had seen practice at the PDSA as a student and called the senior vet at one of their practices to get some advice. She was happy for me to locum for her for one week as a trial. Locuming as a new graduate is not the done thing, but with the right support it is absolutely achievable. It is just really important to be honest about your level of experience... no TPLO's on the first day. Many people think that the PDSA is not an organisation that takes on new graduates. Working for such a busy and dynamic charity is actually the best place for a new graduate, with the scope of surgical experience being one of the most attractive features. This one week locum turned into 2, then 4 and I have just signed a permanent contract with the PDSA.

I have also started on a part-time contract with Vets Now. We have no out of ours work with the PDSA and this is an area I am particularly interested in. Working for a dedicated emergency and critical care company has been an amazing way to expand my clinical skills. That extra little bit of money helps also. Vets Now are not keen to take vets without 2 years experience, but again this is something I have managed to do with the right support. Anything is possible... you just have to ask. It seems working in private practice is where most new graduates end up. There are so many other options out there, you just have to think outside the box slightly.

I get too many people telling me I live to work. However I love the job I do. The sky is the limit and the profession has many avenues to be explored."

Career Options

Years ago the career path as a new vet was fairly clear: most graduates would enter a mixed practice as an assistant, spend a few years honing their general practice skills, possibly moving to another one or two practices, before settling and buying into a partnership. The profession has changed a lot since then and continues to change and adapt at a staggering rate as the expectations of clients, the technological advances and the structure of the industry all change. The traditional mixed practice is rapidly ceasing to exist with a greater number of solely large, equine and small animal practices opening and even the development of single discipline clinics such as veterinary dental practices or cat-only clinics. The role of large corporate groups in the veterinary industry is also an important one and something which is relatively new to the profession in the UK. There are also a multitude of opportunities for veterinary graduates to specialise and the list of the specialisms that one could move into is so long as to constitute another book. Non-traditional or typical career options also exist ranging from government work to roles within biomedical research and the pharmaceutical industry, to the Armed Forces. The opportunities and options open to today's graduates are many and knowing where you will find yourself in ten, five, or even two years time is becoming increasingly difficult. Needless to say, you will be spoilt for choice and the only limit is your own imagination and resourcefulness.

1. *General Practice*

Most vets will start off in 'general practice,' meaning one in which your role is that of a first-opinion GP of which you should all be familiar. This offers graduates the opportunity to consolidate broadly the range of skills learnt at vet school and often acts as the launch pad to other, more specialised, career paths. Many vets actually stay in general practice, content with seeing a range of first opinion cases and often setting up in business themselves via one of the methods we will mention in due course. What type of practice might I work in then? You may choose to work for a traditional partnership, in which the practice is owned by one, two, or more individuals who all have a say in how the practice is run. The advantages of a partnership are that all profits that the practice generates ultimately go to the partners so as a partner there is an obvious direct incentive to develop the business and offer a great service, running it the way you and your partners wish to without outside influence. The potential rewards as a partner in a successful practice are also relatively high, with salaries of £50,000 plus per year average for partners. It is expensive to buy into most partnerships and is an option that is perhaps not suitable to everyone. For a start you must be confident that you will be able to work well with your partner(s) and if things don't go well for the business then the liability rests squarely on the shoulders of the partners in the practice. Another option is to set up a limited company whereby the practice has directors and if the business runs into trouble then the owners have only limited liability. What difference does this make to you as a new graduate? The truth is not much, at least for smaller practices anyway. The difference may come when one starts thinking of working for one of the larger 'corporates' such as CVS or Medivet. These groups own large numbers of clinics across the country each run in a very similar way with similar protocols, preferred drug and equipment lists and a common image to project. The advantages of working for a 'corporate' include good support from a dedicated HR department, a potentially large network of colleagues in other practices to call upon for advice and guidance and the opportunity for promotion and geographical movement within the firm. The majority of practices owned by large companies tend to run themselves fairly autonomously albeit with backup and support from a central head office and certain shared standards and protocols with other practices within the same group. There is, however, little opportunity to 'buy in' as a partner to these larger companies, although equity purchases may be available depending on the individual company concerned. Another type of 'corporate' practice is that of the veterinary franchise, such as Pet Doctors or Vets4Pets. These companies work with you, as a new business owner, to open up your own branch of whichever company it is, with you needing to invest some of your own capital in the business and the franchise providing the remaining start-up capital and administrative support. You are then entitled, as the 'boss' to a proportion of the practice's profits and pay the franchise company an annual fee to handle the back office, administrative matters such as marketing, recruitment paperwork and the like, thus freeing you up to focus on being a great vet.

2. Specialist Practices

There has been an increase in the number of specialist practices offering specific aspects of veterinary care and often used by first-opinion practices as somewhere to refer difficult cases to for more thorough, specialist – and expensive – diagnosis and treatments. The classic example would be a practice such as Davies Veterinary Specialists in Hertfordshire, who accept small animal referrals for everything from internal medicine to orthopaedic surgery. Other practices exist which offer even more of a specific specialism, for example ophthalmology or cardiology. The universities also offer referral services and it was these that used to provide the bulk of the specialist services now available in the UK. As part of your final year clinical training you will be heavily involved with working up and treating such referral cases. Another form of specialism that is becoming more common within the veterinary profession and market is that of clinics that see one species or type of animal. Examples include clinics that see only cats, or 'exotics'. We're all aware of the fact that practices exist that see and treat only small animals or large, whether it be farm or equine or both. Another relatively recent type of 'specialist' practice is that offering out of hours emergency cover for other practices in an area. The leader in this field is Vets Now, who see emergency cases for participating practices and usually make use of the facilities in a specific 'member' practice overnight. If your particular area of interest was emergency veterinary medicine and surgery then such companies can offer a very rewarding career option. As can be appreciated, there are ever more options for 'specialising' as a veterinary surgeon these days and most of us will find ourselves making the decision to 'specialise' early in our careers by either electing to go into large animal or small animal practice. It is, of course, still possible to find positions in traditional mixed practices although these are becoming fewer and there is often some debate as to how much large animal practice actually gets to be seen in such jobs, with one common complaint being that the large animal component tends to simply be "the emergency farm callouts to attend a difficult calving or a colic at 4am!"

The routes into true specialism are, again, many and can include studying for certificates whilst working in private practice to working at a university as both interns and residents, ultimately studying for a diploma in a specific discipline. The main diplomas that specialists aim for are ones conferred by both the American College and European College. A greater number of private referral centres are now offering internships and residencies and, again, the aim here is for candidates to ultimately achieve certificates and diplomas and thus attain specialist status.

Other areas of work

To think of veterinary graduates just engaging in private or specialist practice is to grossly miss the bigger picture and whilst the vast majority of graduates are engaged in practice, a large number are employed by various other sectors where their unique skills are called upon. These include the following:

a) Government positions – these include working for DEFRA, in abattoirs as Official Veterinarians with overall responsibility for ensuring quality assurance in meat production, or at ports overseeing the import and export of animals and animal related goods. The range of roles for vets in important government work includes working for Animal Health, the agency formally known as the State Veterinary Service, and work as Home Office inspectors. There are also numerous opportunities for vets to make a real difference in disease surveillance working for the Veterinary Laboratories Agency (VLA). Having some knowledge of the variety of such roles that vets play in important government work may impress interviewers if you are asked about them.

b) Biomedical industry – pharmaceutical companies and those engaged in research and development of both human and veterinary treatments all employ vets, either as named veterinary surgeons for the purpose of engaging in research using animals, or for their expertise in disciplines such as pathology. As with practice, the opportunity for specialism in this line of work is large. Some vets opt to tread the executive career path, working in management positions

c) Armed Forces – Vets can join the Army as part of the Royal Veterinary Corp. They enter as captains for a four year Short Service Commission, but this may be altered to a regular commission on application

d) Charitable work – there are a number of charitable organisations which employ vets, the most well known being the RSPCA, PDSA, Dogs Trust, and many more

e) Teaching – many graduates enter academia and spend their careers engaged in original research and teaching of undergraduates.

f) Complete change – at this stage it may seem like an impossible consideration to imagine yourself doing something non-veterinary but truth is that a proportion of vets will, at some point in their careers, find themselves changing career altogether and for a variety of reasons ranging from disillusionment with the long hours, pressure and relatively low rewards to lifestyle considerations – for example, to fit in more with raising a young family, or simply for a new challenge. The types of careers that veterinary graduates may find themselves in are many, owing to the fact that vets possess skills that make them very employable across a range of sectors – banking and finance, to, well, anything! Even writing!

Opportunity to travel

A degree in veterinary medicine is a passport to the rest of the world, especially if you graduate from either one of the UK or American schools. With a UK degree many countries, including Australia and New Zealand, will allow you to travel to and work as a vet without sitting additional exams. If this is your plan then we do advise checking with the embassy of the country you intend to visit in order to check visa requirements and the like. We could fill a hundred pages of this book with stories and profiles of vets who are working, or studying for post-graduate qualifications, in far-flung parts of the world, whether it be treating racehorses for Sheikhs in Saudi Arabia, or studying for a residency in small animal internal medicine in the USA. The possibilities are boundless so if you are looking for a profession that is going to enable you to travel widely and support yourself doing an interesting and varied job then veterinary is it!

The plethora of opportunities available to veterinary graduates mean that despite some hidden expenses in the course of training and the relatively large burden of debt that vets start their careers with the employment opportunities are good. Whilst 80% of graduates work in clinical practice a large number of veterinary graduates work in other exciting, and perhaps surprising sectors.

Mick Bailey
BVSc, PhD

Mick graduated from Bristol and is now Professor of Comparative Immunology, researching mucosal immune responses and teaching immunology.

I joined the veterinary course at Bristol in 1974, with the usual intention of becoming a practicing vet. At the time, and through most of the course, it never occurred to me that normal people might consider other options. If I thought about it, I assumed that the only reason for not being in practice would be that you weren't very good at it.

The change happened almost by accident during the final year. Through the course, I'd always been interested in parasitology and immunology and, part way through the year, someone pointed out a PhD advertised at Cambridge for a veterinary graduate to study immune responses to *Strongylus vulgaris* in horses. I applied and was offered the place, and decided to do it because I was interested, not because I had any clear plans about a future career.

The PhD was like any first job – a culture shock, sometimes exciting, sometimes depressing. But by the time it was over I was hooked on the idea that I could get paid for asking questions that there weren't answers to, and for doing experiments to find out about things I was interested in.

Just in case, I did go into mixed practice after the PhD. I didn't want to commit to a research career and then feel later on that I'd missed out on anything. Another culture shock, but the PhD training in information processing (rather than memorising) made it easier to catch up. I enjoyed it, but it didn't offer the freedom of enquiry that I wanted.

After a year, I went back into research, and stayed there, working on the way the gut immune system manages to respond actively and aggressively to pathogens while switching off immune responses to harmless antigens like food and commensal bacteria. The work is relevant to animal diseases but also to human infant allergies and to mucosal vaccines. It's had a real impact on early weaning of piglets, and I still get invited to talk about the research in veterinary and in medical schools. I've always worked on things that I thought were interesting, rather than things other people thought I should work on. That's important: do things because you're interested. I'm also still involved directly with the veterinary profession, although I left the RCVS in 1987, as a member of their Research Subcommittee, responsible for involving the RCVS in UK veterinary research strategy.

The type of work has changed dramatically over the years – the techniques and equipment we use now weren't available when I started, and the questions we can answer now, we couldn't even ask back then. I expect it to change just as much before I retire – by then, we'll be using techniques and working on areas we can't imagine now. Like any other job, research has its ups and downs but, although it sounds like a cliché, it's been exciting and I expect it to stay that way: if it stops being exciting, I'll get out.

So, would I do it again? Every time! A veterinary degree is about much more than veterinary practice. It opens up more options, not less. It's actually one of the most broad-based biology degrees there is: no other degree covers the same breadth of factors affecting animal disease – immunology, microbiology, pathology, nutrition, housing, behaviour, welfare. A veterinary background gives you a different view from a conventional science degree, and both are necessary to make progress in understanding and controlling diseases.

Summary

The veterinary profession is changing rapidly and as such it is as important as ever to be sure of what you're letting yourself in for. A career in veterinary medicine will not guarantee the kind of riches that you could expect from a career in banking, law or medicine and compared to other professions the day to day life of a traditional vet in clinical practice can be long, stressful and occasionally quite lonely. However, most veterinary graduates would say that they are not in the profession for material reasons and are just happy to finally be doing something that they have dreamt of since a very early age. Every day can be totally unique with surprises just a phone call away. Despite the challenges and stress involved it is the satisfaction of doing a great job and striving to improve the lives of millions of pets, production animals and their owners that really drives the profession to do what it does. Veterinary still enjoys a deep respect and admiration from members of the public and it is our duty to uphold the excellent reputation of the profession and to welcome new members. Ask most vets what they would do if they weren't a vet and chances are you'll receive a blank look and an answer along the lines of "I couldn't honestly see myself doing any other job in the world!" That's got to speak volumes. By reading this book and exploring veterinary as a career option you are taking the first few tentative steps into an interesting, sociable, challenging and richly rewarding world. Good luck ☺

Appendix 1

Veterinary Schools

Rather than give you a pointless list of addresses and contact numbers, all of which can be found easily on the vet schools' websites, we have provided a quick reference for the universities' websites:

Royal Veterinary College (RVC) - London	www.rvc.ac.uk
Cambridge Veterinary School	www.vet.cam.ac.uk
Bristol School of Veterinary Science	www.vetschool.bris.ac.uk
Faculty of Veterinary Science, Liverpool	www.liv.ac.uk/vets
Nottingham School of Veterinary Medicine & Science	www.nottingham.ac.uk/vet
The Royal (Dick) School of Veterinary Studies – Edinburgh	www.vet.ed.ac.uk
University of Glasgow Veterinary School	www.gla.ac.uk/vet
Faculty of Veterinary Medicine, University College, Dublin	www.ucd.ie/vetmed
St George's School of Veterinary Medicine – Granada	www.sgu.edu/website/sguwebsite.nsf/svm

Useful Websites
1. Royal College of Veterinary Surgeons (www.rcvs.org.uk)

The RCVS also have a careers page which offers advice and useful links to other helpful and interesting websites (www.rcvs.org.uk/careers)

2. 'Walks of Life' (www.walksoflife.org.uk & www.youtube.com/vetcareers)

3. Defra (www.defra.gov.uk)

4. UCAS (www.ucas.ac.uk)

5. BMAT (www.admissionstests.cambridgeassessment.org.uk/adt/bmat)

Appendix 2
UK Vet School Admissions 2007/2008

UK Vet School Students		Admissions to the 1st year of the veterinary course in 2007/2008			Admissions to the 2nd or later years of the veterinary course in 2007/2008			Students admitted with a degree			Total numbers attending the veterinary course		
		M	F	Total	M	F	Total	M	F	Total	M	F	Total
Bristol	UK	19	92	114	0	0	0	0	8	9	103	424	538
	EU	1	2		0	0		1	0		4	4	
	Overseas	0	0		0	0		0	0		2	1	
Cambridge	UK	13	49	63	1	3	4	1	3	4	100	270	379
	EU	0	0		0	0		0	0		0	5	
	Overseas	1	0		0	0		0	0		1	3	
Edinburgh	UK	19	66	102	1	10	37	2	14	46	98	380	627
	EU	0	2		1	1		1	2		1	12	
	Overseas	2	13		4	20		5	22		16	120	
Glasgow	UK	27	57	137	1	2	9	1	0	54	121	281	584
	EU	1	2		0	0		1	2		1	3	
	Overseas	12	38		1	5		11	39		46	132	
Liverpool	UK	20	80	102	4	18	23	5	20	26	119	411	545
	EU	0	1		0	0		0	0		3	6	
	Overseas	0	1		1	0		1	0		1	5	

UK Vet School Students

		M	F	Total	M	F	Total	M	F	Total	M	F	Total
London	UK	45	152	213	9	23	32	11	29	55	183	865	1149
	EU	0	0		0	0		0	0		3	16	
	Overseas	4	12		0	0		3	12		16	66	
Nottingham	UK	19	99	124	0	0	0	3	21	24	38	168	217
	EU	0	1		0	0		0	0		1	5	
	Overseas	0	5		0	0		0	0		0	5	
TOTALS		183	672	855	23	82	105	46	172	218	857	3182	4039
Percentage (M:F)		21%	79%	100%	22%	78%	100%	21%	79%	100%	21%	79%	100%

(Data reproduced with the permission of Royal College of Veterinary Surgeons)

UK Vet School Students

		Veterinary students taking an intercalated science course in 2007/2008			Number of intercalated degree holders			Numbers of students obtaining a veterinary degree in 2007		
		M	F	Total	M	F	Total	M	F	Total
Bristol	UK	2	18	20	8	22	30	41	63	107
	EU	0	0		0	0		0	1	
	Overseas	0	0		0	0		1	1	
Cambridge	UK	0	0	0	0	0	0	18	52	70
	EU	0	0		0	0		0	0	
	Overseas	0	0		0	0		0	0	
Edinburgh	UK	0	1	1	4	24	29	18	71	109

University	Category	M	F	Total	M	F	Total	M	F	Total
	EU	0	0		0	0		1	4	
	Overseas	0	0		0	1		4	11	
Glasgow	UK	2	2	4	3	3	6	28	52	94
	EU	0	0		0	0		0	0	
	Overseas	0	0		0	0		6	8	
Liverpool	UK	10	10	20	9	25	34	23	79	104
	EU	0	0		0	0		0	0	
	Overseas	0	0		0	0		1	1	
London	UK	2	5	7	15	45	63	27	121	166
	EU	0	0		0	2		0	4	
	Overseas	0	0		0	1		2	12	
Nottingham	UK	n/a	n/a	0	n/a	n/a	0	n/a	n/a	0
	EU	n/a	n/a		n/a	n/a		n/a	n/a	
	Overseas	n/a	n/a		n/a	n/a		n/a	n/a	
TOTALS		**16**	**36**	**52**	**39**	**123**	**162**	**170**	**480**	**650**
Percentage (M:F)		**31%**	**69%**	**100%**	**24%**	**76%**	**100%**	**26%**	**74%**	**100%**

Veterinary Surgeons	2006	2007	2008
Total on Register	21,799	22,162	22,754
New Registrations	1,386	1,324	1,323

(Data reproduced with the permission of Royal College of Veterinary Surgeons)

	2002/03	2003/04	2004/05	2005/06	2006/07	2007/08
UK Graduate New Registrations	493	493	587	565	569	628
Total Number of Registrations	1,172	1,011	1,309	1,386	1,324	1,323
Percentage (New UK graduates: Total)	42%	49%	45%	41%	43%	47%

(Data reproduced with the permission of Royal College of Veterinary Surgeons)

Total numbers at vet school

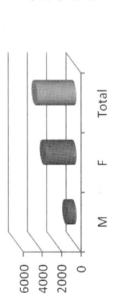

As can be seen from the data, the current ratio of males to females at vet school in the UK stands at approximately 1:3.
(Data reproduced with the permission of Royal College of Veterinary Surgeons)

UCAS University and Course codes:

University & Code	Course Name	Course Code	Course Length (Yrs)	Degree
Royal Veterinary College (R84)	Veterinary Medicine	D100	5	BVetMed
	Combined Degree Programme	D101	6	BVetMed & BSc
	Veterinary Gateway Programme	D102	1	n/a
Cambridge University (C05)	Veterinary Medicine (incl intercalated year)	D100	6	VetMB & MB or MA
Bristol University (B78)	Veterinary Science	D100	5	BVSc
	Veterinary Science with Pre-vet year	D104	6	BVSc
Nottingham University (N84)	Vet Med & Surg (with int BVMed Sci) including pre-year	D104	6	BVMBVS
	Veterinary Medicine & Surgery			

University	Course	Code		Degree
		D100	5	BVMBVS
Liverpool University (L41)	Veterinary Science	D100	5	BVSc
	Veterinary Science with intercalated Hons year	D101	6	BVSc & BSc
Glasgow University (G28)	Veterinary Medicine	D100	5	BVMS
Edinburgh University (E56)	Veterinary Medicine	D100	5	BVM&S
	Veterinary Medicine Graduate Entry	D190	4	BVM&S

Applications to the Veterinary Medicine degree course at University College Dublin (UCD) should be made via the Central Applications Office (CAO). See the website for more information or contact the admissions department directly